James

*The Heritage
of Literature
Series*

SECTION A NO. 9

ADVENTURES AND ENCOUNTERS

LONGMANS, GREEN AND CO. LTD.
39 PATERNOSTER ROW, LONDON, E.C.4
6 OLD COURT HOUSE STREET, CALCUTTA
53 NICOL ROAD, BOMBAY
36A MOUNT ROAD, MADRAS

LONGMANS, GREEN AND CO.
114 FIFTH AVENUE, NEW YORK
221 EAST 20TH STREET, CHICAGO
88 TREMONT STREET, BOSTON

LONGMANS, GREEN AND CO.
480 UNIVERSITY AVENUE, TORONTO

ADVENTURES AND ENCOUNTERS

SELECTED BY

E. W. PARKER, M.C.

AND

A. R. MOON, M.A.

LONGMANS, GREEN AND CO.
LONDON · NEW YORK · TORONTO

First published January 1936

PRINTED IN GREAT BRITAIN BY
NORTHUMBERLAND PRESS LIMITED
NEWCASTLE UPON TYNE

PREFACE

CHANCE happenings and exciting experiences jostle one another in these pages. Often the teller of the tale occupies the centre of the stage, or is at least present as an eye-witness, and it is interesting to discover how skilfully his words conjure up the picture of how it all happened. Sometimes the story is of a thrilling adventure, as when Winston Churchill recalls how he said to himself " *Toujours de l'audace* " and nonchalantly walked past the last Boer sentry without any attempt at concealment. At other times we witness, at second hand, the vivid experiences of childhood, such as Percy Lubbock " discovers " for us when he robs the swan's nest.

It is good for us to understand the workings of other minds, especially of great ones, and to see places through keener eyes than our own. In this way we can lay the foundations of our own knowledge of human nature and of the world around us, so that afterwards when we look at people and things we find we have learnt to see more. Who, after reading the intimate personal records of the life of a great personality, has not had the feeling that the veil has fallen, revealing the portrait of a man whose character he can understand? As with the revelation of character, so it is with places and with the events of history—the strange happening, graphically recalled, awakens our imagination. When once Evelyn has laid his spell upon us, 1666 means something more to us than a mere date; for ever after we have the memory of the moment when we caught our breath and heard the crackling of the burning timbers as the flames leapt high in London's great fire.

ACKNOWLEDGMENTS

For permission to include copyright material, I am indebted to the following:

Messrs. George Allen & Unwin Ltd. for " The Inn at Evening," from *The Path to Rome*, by Hilaire Belloc; Messrs. Thornton Butterworth Ltd. and the Rt. Hon. Winston S. Churchill for " My Escape from the Boers," from *My Early Life*; Messrs. Jonathan Cape Ltd. and Mr. Percy Lubbock for " The Swan's Nest," from *Earlham*; Messrs. Jonathan Cape Ltd. and Mr. Robert Graves for " A Party in the Desert," from *Lawrence and the Arabs*; Messrs. Gerald Duckworth & Co. Ltd. for " Bevis at Work," from *Bevis*, by Richard Jefferies, for " East, Half South," from *The Brassbounder*, by David W. Bone, and for " Nothing but the Truth," from *The Purple Land*, by W. H. Hudson; Messrs. Wm. Heinemann Ltd. for " The Runagates," from *The Inn of Tranquillity*, by John Galsworthy; Messrs. Longmans Green & Co. Ltd. for " Charles II after Worcester," from *King Charles the Second*, by Arthur Bryant; the Author's Executors and Messrs. Macmillan & Co. Ltd. for " The Adder's Sting," from *The Return of the Native*, by Thomas Hardy; Mr. John Masefield for " The China Tea Race," from *The Bird of Dawning*, published by Messrs. Wm. Heinemann Ltd.; Mr. John Murray for " Lapland," from *The Story of San Michele*, by Axel Munthe, and for " My Coronation," from *The Letters of Queen Victoria*.

CONTENTS

CONTENTS

BEVIS AT WORK

ONE morning a large wooden case was brought to the farmhouse, and Bevis, impatient to see what was in it, ran for the hard chisel and the hammer, and would not consent to put off the work of undoing it for a moment. It must be done directly. The case was very broad and nearly square, but only a few inches deep, and was formed of thin boards. They placed it for him upon the floor, and, kneeling down, he tapped the chisel, driving the edge in under the lid, and so starting the nails. Twice he hit his fingers in his haste, once so hard that he dropped the hammer, but he picked it up again and went on as before, till he had loosened the lid all round.

After labouring like this, and bruising his finger, Bevis was disappointed to find that the case only contained a picture which might look very well, but was of no use to him. It was a fine engraving of " An English Merry-making in the Olden Time," and was soon hoisted up and slung to the wall. Bevis claimed the case as his perquisite, and began to meditate what he could do with it. It was dragged from the house into one of the sheds for him, and he fetched the hammer and his own special little hatchet, for his first idea was to split up the boards. Deal splits so easily, it is a pleasure to feel the fibres part, but upon consideration he thought it might do for the roof of a hut, if he could fix it on four stakes, one at each corner.

Away he went with his hatchet down to the withy-bed by the brook (where he intended to build the hut) to cut some stakes and get them ready. The brook made a sharp turn round the withy-bed, enclosing a tongue of ground which was called in the house at home the "Peninsula," because of its shape and being surrounded on three sides by water. This piece of land, which was not all withy, but partly open and partly copse, was Bevis's own territory, his own peculiar property, over which he was autocrat and king.

He flew at once to attack a little fir, and struck it with the hatchet: the first blow cut through the bark and left a "blaze," but the second did not produce anything like so much effect; the third, too, rebounded, though the tree shook to its top. Bevis hit it a fourth time, not at all pleased that the fir would not cut more easily, and then, fancying he saw something floating down the stream, dropped his hatchet and went to the edge to see.

It was a large fly struggling aimlessly, and as it was carried past a spot where the bank overhung and the grasses drooped into the water, a fish rose and took it, only leaving just the least circle of wavelet. Next came a dead, dry twig, which a wood-pigeon had knocked off with his strong wings as he rose out of the willow-top where his nest was. The little piece of wood stayed a while in the hollow where the brook had worn away the bank, and under which was a deep hole; there the current lingered, then it moved quicker, till, reaching a place where the channel was narrower, it began to rush and rotate, and shot past a long green flag bent down, which ceaselessly fluttered in the swift water. Bevis

14

took out his knife and began to cut a stick to make a toy boat, and then, throwing it down, wished he had a canoe to go floating along the stream and shooting over the bay; then he looked up the brook at the old pollard willow he once tried to chop down for that purpose.

The old pollard was hollow, large enough for him to stand inside on the soft, crumbling "touchwood," and it seemed quite dead, though there were green rods on the top, yet it was so hard he could not do much with it, and wearied his arm to no purpose. Besides, since he had grown bigger he had thought it over, and considered that even if he burnt the tree down with fire, as he had half a mind to do, having read that that was the manner of the savages in wild countries, still he would have to stop up both ends with board, and he was afraid that he could not make it water-tight.

And it was only the same reason that stayed his hand from barking an oak or a beech to make a canoe of the bark, remembering that if he got the bark off in one piece the ends would be open and it would not float properly. He knew how to bark a tree quite well, having helped the woodmen when the oaks were thrown, and he could have carried the short ladder out and so cut it high enough up the trunk (while the tree stood). But the open ends puzzled him; nor could he understand nor get anyone to explain to him how the wild men, if they used canoes like this, kept the water out at the end.

Once, too, he took the gouge and the largest chisel from the workshop, and the mallet with the beechwood head, and set to work to dig out a boat from a vast trunk of elm thrown long since, and lying outside the rick-yard, whither it had been drawn under the timber-carriage. Now, the bark had fallen off this piece of timber from decay, and the surface of the wood was scored and channelled by insects which had eaten their way along it. But though these little creatures had had no difficulty, Bevis with his gouge and his chisel and his mallet could make very little impression, and though he chipped out pieces very happily for half an hour, he had only formed a small hole. So that would not do; he left it, and the first shower filled the hole he had cut with water, and how the savages dug out their canoes with flint choppers he could not think, for he could not cut off a willow twig with the sharpest splinter he could find.

Of course, he knew perfectly well that boats are built of plank, but if you try to build one you do not find it so easy; the planks are not to be fitted together by just thinking you will do it. That was more difficult to him than gouging out the huge elm trunk; Bevis could hardly smooth two planks to come together tight at the edge or even to overlap, nor could he bend them up at the end, and altogether it was a very cross-grained piece of work this making a boat.

Pan, the spaniel, sat down on the hard, dry, beaten earth of the workshop, and looked at Bevis puzzling over his plane and his pencil, his footrule, and the paper on which he had sketched his model; then up at Bevis's forehead, frowning over the trouble of it; next Pan curled round and began to bite himself for fleas, pushing up his nostril and snuffling and raging over them. No. This would not do; Bevis could not wait long enough; Bevis liked the sunshine and the grass underfoot. Crash fell the plank and bang went the hammer as he flung it on the bench, and away they tore out into the field, the spaniel rolling in the grass, the boy kicking up the

16

tall dandelions, catching the yellow disk under the toe of his boot and driving it up in the air.

But though thrown aside like the hammer, still the idea slumbered in his mind, and as Bevis stood by the brook, looking across at the old willow, and wishing he had a boat, all at once he thought what a capital raft the picture packing-case would make! The case was much larger than the picture which came in it; it had not perhaps been originally intended for that engraving. It was broad and flat: it had low sides; it would not be water-tight, but perhaps he could make it—yes, it was just the very thing. He would float down the brook on it; perhaps he would cross the Longpond.

Like the wind he raced back home, up the meadow, through the garden, past the cart-house to the shed where he had left the case. He tilted it up against one of the uprights or pillars of the shed, and then stooped to see if daylight was visible anywhere between the planks. There were many streaks of light, chinks which must be caulked, where they did not fit. In the workshop there was a good heap of tow; he fetched it, and immediately began to stuff it in the openings with his pocket-knife. Some of the chinks were so wide, he filled them up with chips of wood, with the tow round the chips, so as to wedge tightly.

The pocket-knife did not answer well. He got a chisel, but that cut the tow, and was also too thick; then he thought of an old table-knife he had seen lying on the garden wall, left there by the man who had been set to weed the path with it. This did much better, but it was tedious work, very tedious work; he was obliged to leave it twice—once to have a swing, and stretch himself; the second time to get a hunch, or cog, as he called it, of bread and butter. He worked so hard he was so hungry. Round the loaf there were indentations, like a cogged wheel, such as the millwright made. He had one of these cogs of bread cut out, and well stuck over with pats of fresh butter, just made and fresh from the churn, not yet moulded and rolled into shape, a trifle salt, but delicious.

Then on again, thrusting the tow in with the knife, till he had used it all, and still there were a few chinks open. He thought he would get some oakum by picking a bit of rope to pieces: there was no old rope about, so he took out his pocket-knife and stole into the wagon-house, where, first looking round to be sure that no one was about, he slashed at the end of a cart-line. The thick rope was very hard, and it was difficult to cut it; it was twisted so tight, and the rain and the sun had toughened it besides, while the surface was case-hardened by rubbing against the straw of the loads it had bound. He haggled it off at last, but when he tried to pick it to pieces he found the larger strands unwound tolerably well, but to divide them and part the fibres was so weari-some and so difficult that he did not know how to manage it. With a nail he hacked at it, and got quite red in the face, but the tough rope was not to be torn into fragments in a minute; he flung it down, then he recollected someone would see it, so he hurled it over the hedge into the lane.

He ran indoors to see if he could find anything that would do instead, and went up into the bench-room where there was another carpenter's bench (put up for amateur work), and hastily turned over everything; then he pulled out the drawer in his mamma's room, the drawer in which she kept odds and ends, and having upset everything, and mixed her treasures, he lighted on some rag which she kept always ready to bind round the fingers that used to get cut so often. For a make-shift this, he thought, would do. He tore a long piece, left the drawer open, and ran to the shed with it. There was enough to fill the last chink he could see; so it was done. But it was a hundred and twenty yards to the brook, and though he could lift the case on one side at a time, he could not carry it.

He sat down on the stool (dragged out from the work-shop) to think; why, of course he would fasten a rope to it, and so haul it along! Looking for a nail in the nail-box on the bench, for the rope must be tied to some-thing, he saw a staple which would do much better than a nail, so he bored two holes with a gimlet, and drove the staple into the raft. There was a cord in the summer-house by the swing, which he used for a lasso—he had made a running noose, and could throw it over anything or anybody who would keep still—this he fetched, and put through the staple. With the cord over his shoulder he dragged the raft by main force out of the shed, across the hard, dry ground, through the gate, and into the field. It came very hard, but it did come, and he thought he should do it.

The grass close to the rails was not long, and the load slipped rather better on it, but farther out into the field it was longer, and the edge of the case began to catch against it; and when he came to the furrows it was as much as he could manage, first to get it down into the furrow, next to lift it up a little, else it would not move, and then to pull it up the slope. By stopping a while and then hauling he moved it across three of the furrows, but now the cord quite hurt his shoulder, and had begun to fray his jacket. When he looked back he was about thirty yards from where he had started, not half-way to the gateway, through which was another meadow, where the mowing grass was still higher.

Bevis sat down on the sward to rest, his face all hot with pulling, and almost thought he should never do it. There was a trail in the grass behind where the raft had passed like that left by a chain harrow. It wanted something to slip on; perhaps rollers would do like those they moved the great pieces of timber on to the saw-pit. As soon as he had got his breath again, Bevis went back to the shed, and searched round for some rollers. He could not find any wood ready that would do, but there was a heap of poles close by. He chose a large, round willow one, carried the stool down to it, got the end up on the stool, and worked away like a slave till he had sawn off three lengths.

These he took to the raft, put one under the front part, and arranged the other two a little way ahead. Next, having brought a stout stake from the shed, he began to lever the raft along, and was delighted at the ease with which it now moved. But this was only the level ground and down the slope of the next furrow, so far it went very well, but there was a difficulty in getting it up the rise. As the grass grew longer, too, the rollers would not roll; and quite tired out with all this work, Bevis flung down his lever, and thought he would go indoors and sit down and play at something else.

First he stepped into the kitchen, as the door was open; it was a step down to it. The low whitewashed ceiling and the beam across it glowed red from the roasting-fire of logs split in four, and built up on the hearth; the flames rushed up the vast, broad chimney—

a bundle of flames a yard high, whose tips parted from the main tongues and rose disjointed for a moment by themselves: the tiny panes of yellowish-green glass, too, in the window reflected the light. Such a fire as makes one's lips moist at the thought of the juicy meats and the subtle sweetness imparted by the wood fuel, which has a volatile fragrance of its own. Bevis thought he would get the old iron spoon, and melt some lead, and cast some bullets in the mould—he had a mould, though they would not let him have a pistol—he knew where there was a piece of lead-pipe, and a battered bit of guttering that came off the house.

Or else he would put in a nail, make it white hot, and hammer it into an arrowhead, using the wrought-iron fire-dog as an anvil. The heat was so great, especially as it was a warm May day, that before he could decide he was obliged to go out of the kitchen, and so wandered into the sitting-room. His fishing-rod stood in the corner where he had left it; he had brought it in because the second joint was splitting, and he intended (as the ferrule was lost) to bind it round and round with copper wire. But he did not feel much inclined to do that either; he had half a mind to go up in the bench-room, and take the lock of the old gun to pieces to see how it worked. Only the stock (with the lock attached) was left; the barrel was gone.

While he was thinking he walked into the parlour, and seeing the bookcase open—the door was lined within with green material—put his hand involuntarily on an old grey book. The covers were grey and worn and loose; the back part had come off; the edges were rough and difficult to turn over, because they had not been cut by machinery; the margin, too, was yellow and frayed.

Bevis's fingers went direct to the rhyme he had read so often, and in an instant everything around him disappeared, room and bookcase and the garden without, and he forgot himself, for he could see the " bolde men in their deeds," he could hear the harper and the minstrel's song, the sound of trumpet and the clash of steel; how—

> As they were drinking ale and wine
> Within Kyng Estmere's halle:
> When will ye marry a wyfe, brother,
> A wyfe to glad us all?

How the kyng and " Adler younge " rode to the wooing, and the fight they had, fighting so courageously against crowds of enemies—

> That soone they have slayne the Kempery men,
> Or forst them forth to flee.

Bevis put himself so into it, that he did it all, *he* bribed the porter, *he* played the harp, and drew the sword; these were no words to him, it was a living picture in which he himself acted.

He was inclined to go up into the garret and fetch down the old cutlass that was there among the lumber, and go forth into the meadow and slash away at " gix " and parsley and burdocks, and kill them all for Kempery men, just as he cut them down before when he was St. George. As he was starting for the cutlass he recollected that the burdocks and the rest were not up high enough yet, the Paynim scoundrels had not grown tall enough in May to be slain with any pleasure, and a sense that you were valiantly swording. Still there was an old wooden bedstead up there, on which he could hoist up a sail, and sail away to any port he chose, to Spain, or Rhodes, or where the lotus-eaters lived. But his mind, so soon as he had put down the grey book, ran still on his raft, and out he raced to see it again, fresh and bright from the rest of leaving it alone for a little while.

RICHARD JEFFERIES—*Bevis*.

THE SWAN'S NEST

THE river at Earlham was simply the river; I never thought of its possessing a name upon the county map. It does possess one, however, and a name not undistinguished among the waters of East Anglia—the river Yare. Early in its course it reaches Earlham; it twinkles over gravel and water-cress to the brick archway of the bridge, turns suddenly black and silent in the fishing-pool, and winds idly away through the Earlham meadows, a full-fed stream, deep enough to carry us in our broad-beamed old boat. Upstream we could not penetrate far; we should soon hear the floor of the river grinding upon our keel. But downstream the waterway is open to us as far as Cringleford mill—quite as much of a voyage as we shall wish to cover and retrace on a fine hot morning.

So at last we may dip down to the sunk fence beyond the west lawn and journey away towards the water-meadows. The park, gently falling to the valley, had the dignity of its fine trees, scattered and grouped here and there; but when you are fairly out on the slope you can hardly call it a real park; it is quite small, it quickly lapses into flat green meadow-land—and here is the pond. Rustling with rushes, starred with water-lilies in the open, the pond would be sure to delay me; it had many attractions, the best of them perhaps the ancient willow-trunk, rooted in the soft bank, which had sunk and sunk as it leaned over the water, till at last it lay at full length upon the surface, with the lily-leaves floating against its bark. A large and beautiful pond it certainly was; it spread out quite near the river, but there was a stretch of thick grass between the two; and so we should skirt round the pond, to reach the boat-house by the thorn on the river-bank. But you cannot neglect the willow-trunk on the way; there seemed always a chance that if you scrambled and sprawled to the end of it you might find that a white water-lily had unfolded within reach of a grabbing hand. It never had; it was so near that you could see the little black-beetles among its golden spikes, but there was no getting possession of it. What should I do with a water-lily, if I did succeed in clutching the stalk? I couldn't say; yet it would be a valuable prize, the thought of it snapping juicily between my fingers is somehow alluring. And then there are the steel-blue dragon-flies, darting and glancing, and there is the yellow fleabane—and then there is the deep shade of the wood that marches to the very verge of the pond, at the farther end of it. Remember this wood of great trees; I say no more of it for the moment, for the boat-house on the river is close at hand, and we all crowd thither and cluster about the low doorway.

Within there was thudding and bumping and lurching, splashes of echoing water, shafts of green twilight; the boat swayed and smacked its lips (so you might say) as we bundled in and disposed ourselves. Somebody stood in the bows to unlock the gate; and it burst open, caught by the stream outside, and the boat pushed forth into the blaze of light, the water-cool breezes, the clean smell of the draggled weeds. Light and air, the silent movement, the wild and nameless fragrances—they make a penetrating experience. The water talked beneath us as the boat swung round into the stream; and immediately the familiar landscape was changed before our eyes, the fields and woods beyond the low banks seemed to have drawn apart with a new character. Committed to the flow of the stream, one looks back on the green world as though one had left it; to float upon water is as detaching, as liberating as to soar in air. Those woods, that flat marshland, now belong to another sphere; I survey it with curiosity, almost wishing to return to it already, so inviting it seems to enterprise and discovery. But here meanwhile is the sphere of the water-world, with its strange and lovely treasures; trailing my hands in its delicious chill, I can soon be lost in the landscape of the river-floor.

Shallow and pool, pool and shallow, the river coiled its way through the hollow land. Outside the boat-house the gravelly bottom was full in view, only blurred a little by the twist and swirl in the clear glass of the water. Do you know that broad-leaved plant, bright green, translucent, that grows in thick drifts along the bed of the stream, never touching the surface?—and the fine feathery thing, a darker green, eternally pulled by the current, like a thicket through which a wind never ceases to blow?—and the stalks of the arrowhead, that climb to the upper air and are shaken there by a constant little breeze, it would seem, which is not really a breeze but the same secret tug of the stream below?—and the perpetual flitting of tiny shadows over the gravel and sand, as the minnows dart from under our monstrous hull, the leviathan that pushes among their cressy islets? The only sound in the quiet valley was the measured cluck of our clumsy old rowlocks; the reedy pastures were deserted, there wasn't a house or a cottage in sight; the tawny cows stood stock-still, solemnly eyeing us as we passed. And then, as we steered round a swinging bend of the river, the sunlit floor had disappeared and there was nothing but blackness beneath us, thick darkness of water unbroken by reed or rush—a deep pool, and you could plunge the oar down and down, farther and farther into the bottomless mud; and the next moment, perhaps, the boat was almost scraping the clean gravel again, and the smooth bottle-green reed-stems stood out into the water away from the bank; and so the river went winding on its leisurely way, and after ever so long you still saw the boat-house within easy hail, just across the breadth of a single meadow.

There was a reed-bed that appeared very soon on the right, a patch of swamp covered densely with those great reeds like gigantic blades of grass, each with its mop of pinkish plume streaming in the wind. A small jungle of undrained swamp, tangled with thorn-bushes—I take a deep interest in it by reason of an unforgettable passage in the past. Mark the great flattened platform of dead rushes, close to the water's edge, almost hidden by the plumy reed-forest. It is the nest of a swan—empty now and abandoned, to be sure; but if you had come here earlier in the year you would have been met in midstream by the master of the place, the hissing and ruffling swan, and you might well have thought twice before you faced his challenge. I, let me tell you, had faced it; but I admit that I had had powerful support. We were not often at Earlham in birds'-nesting time; and the thrill was the keener when I did get the chance, twice or thrice, of an adventure among the birds of the

27

swamp and the water-meadow. For the quest of the swan I had the company of friend Sidell the butler—the man of nerve, of cool and masterful decision. He met and confronted the passionate fowl with a composure that disconcerted it entirely, and I followed him in easy confidence.

The swan breathed fury, puffing out his magnificent wings; and then he was quite taken aback by Sidell's assurance, and could only sail helplessly to and fro, pouting and hissing, while we landed at the nest; and somehow we must have dislodged his mate, for I remember the sight of the great discoloured eggs, three or four, that lay in the high-piled nest. If it should appear that one of the eggs was addled I had leave to take it; but how are you to know whether an egg is addled while the bird is still sitting hopefully on them all? It is possible, I held, to make certain by shaking the eggs sharply, one by one; the good egg gives no sound, the ripening chick is firmly embedded within; but in the bad you can hear the slop and jumble of the rotting contents, from which no offspring is to be expected. I applied the test accordingly, and one of the eggs was at any rate addled by the time I had done with it. I bore it off, and I have not forgotten the afternoon that was spent in draining the huge malodorous shell. So to you I have discovered (you recognize the quotation) that swan's nest among the reeds.

PERCY LUBBOCK—*Earlham.*

EARLY LIFE OF CHARLES DICKENS

JAMES LAMERT, the relative who had lived with us in Bayham Street, knowing what our domestic circumstances then were, proposed that I should go into the blacking warehouse, to be as useful as I could, at a salary, I think, of six shillings a week. I am not clear whether it was six or seven. I am inclined to believe, from my uncertainty on this head, that it was six at first, and seven afterwards. At any rate, the offer was accepted very willingly by my father and mother, and on a Monday morning I went down to the blacking warehouse to begin my business life.

It is wonderful to me how I could have been so easily cast away at such an age. It is wonderful to me that, even after my descent into the poor little drudge I had been since we came to London, no one had compassion enough on me—a child of singular abilities: quick, eager, delicate, and soon hurt, bodily or mentally—to suggest that something might have been spared, as certainly it might have been, to place me at any common school. Our friends, I take it, were tired out. No one made any sign. My father and mother were quite satisfied. They could hardly have been more so, if I had been twenty years of age, distinguished at a grammar school, and going to Cambridge.

The blacking warehouse was the last house on the left-hand side of the way, at old Hungerford Stairs. It was a crazy, tumble-down old house, abutting of course on the river, and literally overrun with rats. Its wainscotted rooms and its rotten floors and staircase, and the old grey rats swarming down in the cellars, and the sound of their squeaking and scuffling coming up the stairs at all times, and the dirt and decay of the place, rise up visibly before me, as if I were there again. The counting-house was on the first floor, looking over the coal-barges and the river. There was a recess in it, in which I was to sit and work. My work was to cover the pots of paste-blacking: first with a piece of oil-paper, and then with a piece of blue paper; to tie them round with a string; and then to clip the paper close and neat all round, until it looked as smart as a pot of ointment from an apothecary's shop. When a certain number of grosses of pots had attained this pitch of perfection, I was to paste on each a printed label; and then go on again with more pots. Two or three other boys were kept at similar duty downstairs on similar wages. One of them came up, in a ragged apron and a paper cap, on the first Monday morning, to show me the trick of using the string and tying the knot. His name was Bob Fagin; and I took the liberty of using his name, long afterwards, in *Oliver Twist*.

Our relative had kindly arranged to teach me something in the dinner-hour; from twelve to one, I think it was; every day. But an arrangement so incompatible with counting-house business soon died away, from no fault of his or mine; and for the same reason, my small work-table, and my grosses of pots, my papers, string, scissors, paste-pot and labels, by little and little, vanished out of the recess in the counting-house, and kept company with the other small work-tables, grosses of pots, papers, string, scissors and paste-pots downstairs. It was not long before Bob Fagin and I, and another boy whose name was Paul Green, but who was currently believed to have been christened Poll (a belief which I transferred, long afterwards, again, to Mr. Sweedlepipe, in *Martin Chuzzlewit*), worked generally, side by side. Bob Fagin was an orphan, and lived with his brother-in-law, a waterman. Poll Green's father had the additional distinction of being a fireman, and was employed at Drury Lane theatre; where another relation of Poll's, I think his little sister, did imps in the pantomimes.

No words can express the secret agony of my soul as I sank into this companionship; compared these everyday associates with those of my happier childhood; and felt my early hopes of growing up to be a learned and distinguished man crushed in my breast. The deep remembrance of the sense I had of being utterly neglected and hopeless; of the shame I felt in my position; of the misery it was to my young heart to believe that, day by day, what I had learned, and thought, and delighted in, and raised my fancy and my emulation up by, was passing away from me, never to be brought back any more; cannot be written. My whole nature was so penetrated with the grief and humiliation of such considerations, that even now, famous and caressed and happy, I often forget in my dreams that I have a dear wife and children; even that I am a man; and wander desolately back to that time of my life.

My mother and my brothers and sisters (excepting Fanny in the royal academy of music) were still encamped, with a young servant-girl from Chatham Workhouse, in the two parlours in the emptied house in Gower

Street North. It was a long way to go and return within the dinner-hour, and, usually, I either carried my dinner with me, or went and bought it at some neighbouring shop. In the latter case, it was commonly a saveloy and a penny loaf; sometimes, a fourpenny plate of beef from a cook's shop; sometimes, a plate of bread and cheese, and a glass of beer, from a miserable old public-house over the way; the Swan, if I remember right, or the Swan and something else that I have forgotten. Once, I remember tucking my own bread (which I had brought from home in the morning) under my arm, wrapped up in a piece of paper like a book, and going into the best dining-room in Johnson's alamode beef-house in Clare Court, Drury Lane, and magnificently ordering a small plate of alamode beef to eat with it. What the waiter thought of such a strange little apparition, coming in all alone, I don't know; but I can see him now, staring at me as I ate my dinner, and bringing up the other waiter to look. I gave him a halfpenny, and I wish, now, that he hadn't taken it. . . .

My own exclusive breakfast, of a penny cottage loaf and a pennyworth of milk, I provided for myself. I kept another small loaf, and a quarter of a pound of cheese, on a particular shelf of a particular cupboard: to make my supper on when I came back at night. They made a hole in the six or seven shillings, I know well; and I was out at the blacking warehouse all day, and had to support myself upon that money all the week. I suppose my lodging was paid for, by my father. I certainly did not pay it myself; and I certainly had no other assistance whatever (the making of my clothes, I think, excepted), from Monday morning until Saturday night. No advice, no counsel, no encouragement, no consolation, no support, from anyone that I can call to mind, so help me God.

Sundays Fanny and I passed in the prison.[1] I was at the academy in Tenterden Street, Hanover Square, at nine o'clock in the morning, to fetch her; and we walked back there together at night.

I was so young and childish, and so little qualified—how could I be otherwise?—to undertake the whole charge of my own existence that, in going to Hungerford Stairs of a morning, I could not resist the stale pastry put out at half-price on trays at the confectioners' doors in Tottenham Court Road; and I often spent in that the money I should have kept for my dinner. Then I went without my dinner, or bought a roll, or a slice of pudding. There were two pudding shops between which I was divided, according to my finances. One was in a court close to St. Martin's Church (at the back of the church), which is now removed altogether. The pudding at that shop was made with currants, and was rather a special pudding, but was dear: two penn'orth not being larger than a penn'orth of more ordinary pudding. A good shop for the latter was in the Strand, somewhere near where the Lowther Arcade is now.[2] It was a stout, hale pudding, heavy and flabby; with great raisins in it, stuck in whole, at great distances apart. It came up hot, at about noon every day; and many and many a day did I dine off it.

We had half an hour, I think, for tea. When I had money enough, I used to go to a coffee-shop, and have half a pint of coffee, and a slice of bread and butter. When I had no money, I took a turn in Covent Garden Market,

[1] The Marshalsea.
[2] It no longer exists.

and stared at the pineapples. The coffee-shops to which I most resorted were, one in Maiden Lane; one in a court (non-existent now) close to Hungerford Market; and one in St. Martin's Lane, of which I only recollect that it stood near the church, and that in the door there was an oval glass plate, with COFFEE-ROOM painted on it, addressed towards the street. If I ever find myself in a very different kind of coffee-room now, but where there is such an inscription on glass, and read it backward on the wrong side MOOR-EEFFOC (as I often used to do then, in a dismal reverie), a shock goes through my blood.

I know I do not exaggerate, unconsciously and unintentionally, the scantiness of my resources and the difficulties of my life. I know that if a shilling or so were given me by anyone, I spent it in a dinner or a tea. I know that I worked, from morning to night, with common men and boys, a shabby child. I know that I tried, but ineffectually, not to anticipate my money, and to make it last the week through by putting it away in a drawer I had in the counting-house, wrapped into six little parcels, each parcel containing the same amount, and labelled with a different day. I know that I have lounged about the streets, insufficiently and unsatisfactorily fed. I know that, but for the mercy of God, I might easily have been, for any care that was taken of me, a little robber or a little vagabond.

But I held some station at the blacking warehouse too. Besides that my relative at the counting-house did what a man so occupied, and dealing with a thing so anomalous, could, to treat me as one upon a different footing from the rest, I never said, to man or boy, how it was that I came to be there, or gave the least indication of being sorry that I was there. That I suffered in secret, and that I suffered exquisitely, no one ever knew but I. How much I suffered, it is, as I have said already, utterly beyond my power to tell. No man's imagination can overstep the reality. But I kept my own counsel, and I did my work. I knew from the first that, if I could not do my work as well as any of the rest, I could not hold myself above a slight and contempt. I soon became at least as expeditious and as skilful with my hands as either of the other boys. Though perfectly familiar with them, my conduct and manners were different enough from theirs to place a space between us. They, and the men, always spoke of me as " the young gentleman." A certain man (a soldier once) named Thomas, who was the foreman, and another named Harry, who was the carman and wore a red jacket, used to call me " Charles " sometimes, in speaking to me; but I think it was mostly when we were very confidential, and when I had made some efforts to entertain them over our work with the results of some of the old readings, which were fast perishing out of my mind. Poll Green uprose once, and rebelled against the " young-gentleman " usage; but Bob Fagin settled him speedily.

JOHN FORSTER—*The Life of Charles Dickens.*

THE VILLAGE IDIOT

TO THE HON. DAINES BARRINGTON

SELBORNE,
Dec. 12, 1775.

DEAR SIR,—We had in this village, more than twenty
years ago, an idiot boy, whom I well remember, who,
from a child, showed a strong propensity to bees; they
were his food, his amusement, his sole object. And as
people of this cast have seldom more than one point of
view, so this lad exerted all his few faculties on this one
pursuit. In the winter he dozed away his time, within
his father's house, by the fireside, in a kind of torpid
state, seldom departing from the chimney corner; but
in the summer he was all alert, and in quest of his
game in the fields and on sunny banks. Honey-bees,
humble-bees, and wasps were his prey wherever he
found them: he had no apprehensions from their
stings, but would seize them with naked hands, and
at once disarm them of their weapons, and suck their
bodies for the sake of their honey-bags. Sometimes he
would fill his bosom, between his shirt and his skin,
with a number of these captives; and sometimes would
confine them in bottles. He was a very *merops apiaster*,
or bee-bird; and very injurious to men that kept bees;
for he would slide into their bee-gardens, and sitting

down before the stools, would rap with his finger on the hives, and so take the bees as they came out. He has been known to overturn hives for the sake of honey, of which he was passionately fond. Where metheglin[1] was making, he would linger round the tubs and vessels, begging a draught of what he called bee-wine. As he ran about he used to make a humming noise with his lips, resembling the buzzing of bees. This lad was lean and sallow, and of a cadaverous complexion; and, except in his favourite pursuit, in which he was wonderfully adroit, discovered no manner of understanding. . . .

When a tall youth, he was removed from hence to a distant village, where he died, as I understand, before he arrived at manhood.

[1] Metheglin: spiced mead.

GILBERT WHITE—*The Natural History of Selborne.*

CHARLES II AFTER WORCESTER

As the last streaks of daylight, September 3rd, 1651, fell
on the Worcestershire landscape, a tall dark fugitive
drew in his horse on a lonely heath. About him
clustered some sixty lords and officers, whose looks told
a tale of peril and defeat.

At that moment the young King of England had
touched a lower point than any to which his twenty-one
chequered and poverty-stricken years had yet brought
him. A few weeks before he had ridden at the head
of a Scottish army along the moorland road by Shap
Fell, watching, across the unclouded atmosphere of
summer, the distant Derbyshire heights beckoning him
on to London and a golden crown. Now his gallant
gamble had ended in dust. All day he had fought at
the head of outnumbered and despairing men as Crom-
well's net closed in on Worcester. Only at evening, as
the shattered Scots poured out through St. Martin's
Gate, had King Charles, protesting that he would rather
die than see the consequences of so fatal a day, been
swept by the rout from the doomed city.

At Barbourne Bridge, where the grass highway to the
north was crowded with flying men, there had been a
hasty consultation. The King himself had wished to
ride alone to London, trusting to arrive before news of
the battle and so take ship to France. But the day was

already waning, and his companions had dissuaded him from this desperate course. Leaving the main line of fugitives to the west, they rode with him across a land of wooded valleys and little hills, until at nightfall they reached Kinver Heath. Here the scout, who was leading, admitted that he was lost.

In the confusion that followed, the Earl of Derby brought forward a Catholic gentleman, Charles Giffard, owner of a remote house in Shropshire, near which he had found shelter a few days before. To Giffard and his servant, Yates, a poor rustic skilful in the ways of that country, the fugitives entrusted themselves. So guided they came down into the hidden lands below. As complete darkness fell, romance spread her cloak over the King and hid him from the thousand eyes that sought him.

Nobody suspected the little party of Cavaliers, who walked their horses through the streets of sleeping Stourbridge. At an inn near Wordsley, the King stopped for a hasty tankard of ale: then rode on through the night, a crust of bread in one hand and meat in the other. Giffard rode at his side, telling him of the secret hiding-places of Whiteladies and Boscobel, while the broken lords and officers trotted behind. For some hours they followed a maze of winding lanes, till they came to the edge of Brewood Forest. Here, fifty miles from the battlefield, and a little before dawn, the tired King saw the dark outlines of the ruined monastery of Whiteladies.

The clatter of hooves and the whispered calls of Giffard brought down the Penderels, the poor Catholic woodcutters who tenanted the house. To these humble folk the great personages, crowding into the hall, turned

for help and advice. While a hasty message was sent
to bring William, the eldest of the five Penderel brothers,
from Boscobel, the King, in an inner chamber, broke his
fast on sack and biscuits. A few minutes later Lord
Derby brought in William and Richard Penderel to
him, telling them that they must have a care of him
and preserve him. To this they proudly and gladly
assented. Richard went out to fetch some country
clothes, while the King stripped and put on a rough
noggen shirt. The first lines of dawn were appearing
when Richard returned with an old sweaty leather
doublet, a green, threadbare coat and a greasy steeple
hat without band or lining. Lord Wilmot, the stoutest
and merriest of the fugitives, began to cut the royal
locks with a knife, but did the job so badly that Richard
was commanded to finish it, which he did in great pride
with a basin and a pair of shears. Placing his hands
up the chimney, Charles, who, despite peril and weariness, could not refrain from laughing, completed his
make-up by blacking his face. Then, while his companions rode off to join the flying Scots, he went out
into the dawn with Richard Penderel and a bill-hook.

It was raining. All day the King crouched in the
damp undergrowth of a little wood, called Spring
Coppice. About midday Penderel's sister-in-law, Eliza-
beth Yates, brought him a blanket to sit on and a mess
of milk, butter and eggs. She told him news of the
world outside the woods—of long streams of Scottish
fugitives and pursuing Roundheads and of search-parties
already at Whiteladies. Afterwards he fell into a broken
slumber. . . .

In the intervals of sleep the King talked to Penderel.
He had still hopes of reaching London and there taking

40

ship for France, but his companion knew of no one on that road who could assist him. It was therefore decided that he should make for Wales, where he had many friends, and that Penderel should escort him that night to Madeley, ten miles to the west, where a Catholic gentleman of his acquaintance might secure them a passage across the Severn.

A little before dusk the two left the wood and made their way across a heath to Hobbal Grange, the cottage where Richard lived with his widowed mother. The old peasant came out to welcome her King, blessing God that she had raised up children to succour him in his time of need. She gave him bread, cheese and a fricassee of bacon and eggs, and wondered to see his appetite, half regal and wholly boyish. While she waited at the table, her son-in-law, Francis Yates—who not long after was hanged at Oxford for his share in the affair— came in with thirty pieces of silver, his all, which he offered to the King. The latter, who—though he perhaps did not realize the full grandeur of the sacrifice— was not unacquainted with poverty, accepted ten of them in his necessity.

The night was pitch black, and Charles, after two days of continuous action and exposure, was tired out. He and Penderel made their way across country, avoiding the haunts of men and clambering the wet fences and pales of remote enclosures. After a few miles, the trackway they were following dipped down to bridge a stream, beside which stood a mill. The miller, hearing footsteps, appeared at the door, and called on them to stop. Instead of obeying, they ran blindly past him. The lane beyond the river was muddy and steep, and the darkness was such that Charles had nothing to guide him but the rustling of Penderel's breeches ahead and the miller's footsteps behind. When his breath and courage could carry him no longer, he flung himself into the hedge and waited for the end. Here Penderel joined him, and the two lay listening for their pursuer. But all was quiet, and after a time they resumed their journey through the briary, dripping night. Poor Charles was now in despair. His ill-made country shoes so racked his feet that he threw them away and walked in his slashed stockings. His nose began to bleed, his head throbbed and his limbs trembled with cold and weariness. "Many times he cast himself upon the ground with a desperate and obstinate resolution to rest there till the morning that he might shift with less torment, what hazard so ever he ran. But his stout guide still prevailed with him to make a new attempt, sometimes promising him that the way should be better, sometimes assuring him that he had but a little farther to go." Shortly after midnight they came to Madeley.

At the edge of the village Penderel left the King in hiding and made his way to Francis Wolfe's house. The old gentleman—he was sixty-nine, and lived to see the Restoration—came to the door. Penderel asked him if he would help a Royalist fugitive of rank to cross the Severn. Wolfe replied that the town was full of troops, and all the passages across the river guarded, and that he would not undertake so perilous a task for anyone but the King himself. But when Penderel blurted out the truth, he expressed his readiness to venture his life and all that he had.

As the priest-holes in the house were known, the Wolfes and their daughter, Anne, sheltered the King all that day in a hayloft. In the evening they brought

him food and money, and new shoes and stockings.
Then, as the passage of the Severn was judged impossible, the two travellers started on the return journey
for Boscobel. At Evelith Mill, fearing their challenger
of the previous night, they left the roadway, intending
to ford the river above the bridge. Here Penderel's
courage, for the first and last time, failed him. The
heavy rain had swollen the little stream, and, child of
the Midlands that he was, he confided that he could
not swim and that it was a scurvy river. Thirty years
afterwards Charles dictated the story of that passage to
Pepys. "So I told him that the river, being but a little
one, I would undertake to help him over. Upon which
we went over some closes to the river side, and I, entering the river first to see whether I could myself go over,
who knew how to swim, found it was but a little above
my middle, and, thereupon, taking Richard Penderel
by the hand, I helped him over." At about three o'clock
that morning, they passed the gateway of Whiteladies
and came into the woods between that place and
Boscobel.

Leaving the King in the wood, Penderel went on to
Boscobel to consult his brother as to the next step in
their desperate enterprise. Here news awaited him.
Lord Wilmot had found a refuge at the house of a neighbouring Catholic gentleman, Mr. Whitgreave of Moseley
Hall, through the offices of Father Huddleston, a priest,
who lived there. The other piece of news was that
Colonel Careless, who two days before had led the last
charge over the cobblestones of Worcester, was in hiding
at Boscobel.

Careless accompanied Penderel back to the wood. He
found the King, at the first stroke of dawn, sitting forlorn

on a tree-stump, and could not refrain from weeping at the sight. The three then walked together across the high ground towards Boscobel, looking back, as the sun touched the Wrekin, on the far Welsh mountains beyond the Severn.

At Boscobel, a black and white hunting-lodge amid a jumble of barns and hayricks, the King breakfasted off bread, cheese and small beer. Joan Penderel, William's wife, washed and dressed his feet, cutting the blisters and inserting pads of paper between his toes. Then, as it was probable that the house would be searched by one of the numerous companies of soldiers in the neighbourhood, Charles and Careless went out again into the wood.

At the edge of the copse, overlooking the highway, was an old hollow oak. Into this, at Careless's suggestion, they climbed. The road below was soon busy with passers-by, and, through the veil of leaves that concealed them, they could see a party of soldiers searching the woods, where the Penderels, to allay suspicion, were "peaking up and down" with their nut-hooks. After a time Charles, worn out, fell asleep with his head in Careless's lap. As the hours passed and the King's fitful slumber continued, Careless's supporting arm became completely numbed. With infinite difficulty he awoke him, motioning him to silence lest the troopers below should hear.

At nightfall, when the seekers had gone home to prepare for the Sabbath, the Penderels brought a ladder to the tree, and Charles and Careless, tired, cramped and hungry, returned to Boscobel. They passed through the big parlour of the house—it still stands—and up the stairs to a long attic gallery, used for storing cheeses.

Here Mrs. Penderel, whom Charles christened Dame Joan, brought them a supper of chickens. Afterwards, as the night was fine, Charles sat for a while drinking wine in the garden, where Humphrey Penderel, the miller, came with news. While in the town that day, he had been questioned by a republican officer, who suspected that he knew of the King's whereabouts. Humphrey had stoutly denied all knowledge, where-upon the officer showed him a proclamation, threatening death to all who should aid " Charles Stuart, a long dark man, above two yards high," and offering a reward of £1,000 to anyone who should betray him. On hearing this Charles could not help reflecting on the temptation to which the poor men who sheltered him were exposed, but Careless, divining his thoughts, assured him that had the reward been a thousand times as great it could not have shaken their fidelity.

ARTHUR BRYANT—*King Charles the Second.*

MY ESCAPE FROM THE BOERS

During the first three weeks of my captivity, although I was a party to all plans of revolt or escape, I was engaged in arguing with the Boer Authorities that they should release me as a Press Correspondent. They replied that I had forfeited my non-combatant status by the part I had taken in the armoured train fight. I contended that I had not fired a shot and had been taken unarmed. This was strictly true. But the Natal newspapers had been captured by the Boers. These contained glowing accounts of my activities, and attributed the escape of the engine and the wounded entirely to me. General Joubert therefore intimated that even if I had not fired a shot myself, I had injured the Boer operations by freeing the engine, and that I must therefore be treated as a prisoner-of-war. As soon as I learned of this decision, in the first week of December, I resolved to escape.

I shall transcribe what I wrote at the time where I cannot improve upon it.

"The State Model Schools stood in the midst of a quadrangle, and were surrounded on two sides by an iron grille and on two by a corrugated-iron fence about ten feet high. These boundaries offered little obstacle to anyone who possessed the activity of youth, but the fact that they were guarded on the inside by sentries, fifty yards apart, armed with rifle and revolver, made them a well-nigh insuperable barrier. No walls are so hard to pierce as living walls.

" After anxious reflection and continual watching, it was discovered by several of the prisoners that when the sentries along the eastern side walked about on their beats they were at certain moments unable to see the top of a few yards of the wall near the small circular lavatory office which can be seen on the plan.[1] The electric lights in the middle of the quadrangle brilliantly lighted the whole place, but the eastern wall was in shadow. The first thing was therefore to pass the two sentries near the office. It was necessary to hit off the exact moment when both their backs should be turned together. After the wall was scaled we should be in the garden of the villa next door. There the plan came to an end. Everything after this was vague and uncertain. How to get out of the garden, how to pass unnoticed through the streets, how to evade the patrols that surrounded the town, and above all how to cover the two hundred and eighty miles to the Portuguese frontier, were questions which would arise at a later stage."

" Together with Captain Haldane and Lieutenant Brockie I made an abortive attempt, not pushed with any decision, on December 11. There was no difficulty in getting into the circular office. But to climb out of it over the wall was a hazard of the sharpest character. Anyone doing so must at the moment he was on the top of the wall be plainly visible to the sentries fifteen yards away, if they were in the right place and happened

[1] See plan on page 190.

to look! Whether the sentries would challenge or fire depended entirely upon their individual dispositions, and no one could tell what they would do. Nevertheless I was determined that nothing should stop my taking the plunge the next day. As the 12th wore away my fears crystallized more and more into desperation. In the evening, after my two friends had made an attempt, but had not found the moment propitious, I strolled across the quadrangle and secreted myself in the circular office. Through an aperture in the metal casing of which it was built I watched the sentries. For some time they remained stolid and obstructive. Then all of a sudden one turned and walked up to his comrade, and they began to talk. Their backs were turned."

"Now or never! I stood on a ledge, seized the top of the wall with my hands, and drew myself up. Twice I let myself down again in sickly hesitation, and then with a third resolve scrambled up and over. My waistcoat got entangled with the ornamental metal-work on the top. I had to pause for an appreciable moment to extricate myself. In this posture I had one parting glimpse of the sentries still talking with their backs turned fifteen yards away. One of them was lighting his cigarette, and I remember the glow on the inside of his hands as a distinct impression which my mind recorded. Then I lowered myself lightly down into the adjoining garden and crouched among the shrubs. I was free! The first step had been taken, and it was irrevocable. It now remained to await the arrival of my comrades. The bushes in the garden gave a good deal of cover, and in the moonlight their shadows fell dark on the ground. I lay here for an hour in great impatience and anxiety. People were continually moving about in the garden, and once a man came and apparently looked straight at me only a few yards away. Where were the others? Why did they not make the attempt? "

" Suddenly I heard a voice from within the quadrangle say, quite loud, ' All up.' I crawled back to the wall. Two officers were walking up and down inside, jabbering Latin words, laughing and talking all manner of nonsense—amid which I caught my name. I risked a cough. One of the officers immediately began to chatter alone. The other said, slowly and clearly, ' They cannot get out. The sentry suspects. It's all up. Can you get back again? ' But now all my fears fell from me at once. To go back was impossible. I could not hope to climb the wall unnoticed. There was no helpful ledge on the outside. Fate pointed onwards. Besides, I said to myself, ' Of course, I shall be recaptured, but I will at least have a run for my money.' I said to the officers, ' I shall go on alone.'

" Now I was in the right mood for these undertakings —failure being almost certain, no odds against success affected me. All risks were less than the certainty. A glance at the plan will show that the gate which led into the road was only a few yards from another sentry. I said to myself, ' *Toujours de l'audace*,' put my hat on my head, strode into the middle of the garden, walked past the windows of the house without any attempt at concealment, and so went through the gate and turned to the left. I passed the sentry at less that five yards. Most of them knew me by sight. Whether he looked at me or not I do not know, for I never turned my head. I restrained with the utmost difficulty an impulse to run. But after walking a hundred yards and hearing no

49   D

challenge, I knew that the second obstacle had been surmounted. I was at large in Pretoria.

"I walked on leisurely through the night, humming a tune and choosing the middle of the road. The streets were full of burghers, but they paid no attention to me. Gradually I reached the suburbs, and on a little bridge I sat down to reflect and consider. I was in the heart of the enemy's country. I knew no one to whom I could apply for succour. Nearly three hundred miles stretched between me and Delagoa Bay. My escape must be known at dawn. Pursuit would be immediate. Yet all exits were barred. The town was picketed, the country was patrolled, the trains were searched, the line was guarded. I wore a civilian brown flannel suit. I had seventy-five pounds in my pocket and four slabs of chocolate, but the compass and the map which might have guided me, the opium tablets and meat lozenges which should have sustained me, were in my friends' pockets in the State Model Schools. Worst of all, I could not speak a word of Dutch or Kaffir, and how was I to get food or direction?

"But when hope had departed, fear had gone as well. I formed a plan. I would find the Delagoa Bay Railway. Without map or compass, I must follow that in spite of the pickets. I looked at the stars. Orion shone brightly. Scarcely a year before he had guided me when lost in the desert to the banks of the Nile. He had given me water. Now he should lead to freedom. I could not endure the want of either.

"After walking south for half a mile I struck the railway. Was it the line to Delagoa Bay or the Pietersburg branch? If it were the former, it should run east. But, so far as I could see, this line ran northwards. Still, it might be only winding its way out among the hills. I resolved to follow it. The night was delicious. A cool breeze fanned my face, and a wild feeling of exhilaration took hold of me. At any rate, I was free, if only for an hour. That was something. The fascination of the adventure grew. Unless the stars in their courses fought for me, I could not escape. Where, then, was the need of caution? I marched briskly along the line. Here and there the lights of a picket fire gleamed. Every bridge had its watchers. But I passed them all, making very short *détours* at the dangerous places, and really taking scarcely any precautions. Perhaps that was the reason I succeeded.

"As I walked I extended my plan. I could not march three hundred miles to the frontier. I would board a train in motion and hide under the seats, on the roof, on the couplings—anywhere. I thought of Paul Bultitude's escape from school in *Vice Versa*. I saw myself emerging from under the seat, and bribing or persuading some fat first-class passenger to help me. What train should I take? The first, of course. After walking for two hours I perceived the signal lights of a station. I left the line, and circling round it, hid in the ditch by the track about two hundred yards beyond the platform. I argued that the train would stop at the station and that it would not have got up too much speed by the time it reached me. An hour passed. I began to grow impatient. Suddenly I heard the whistle and the approaching rattle. Then the great yellow head-lights of the engine flashed into view. The train waited five minutes at the station, and started again with much noise and steaming. I crouched by the track. I rehearsed the act in my mind. I must wait until the engine had passed, otherwise I should be seen. Then I must make a dash for the carriages.

"The train started slowly, but gathered speed sooner than I had expected. The flaring lights drew swiftly near. The rattle became a roar. The dark mass hung for a second above me. The engine-driver silhouetted against his furnace glow, the black profile of the engine, the clouds of steam rushed past. Then I hurled myself on the trucks, clutched at something, missed, clutched again, missed again, grasped some sort of hand-hold, was swung off my feet—my toes bumping on the line, and with a struggle seated myself on the couplings of the fifth truck from the front of the train. It was a goods train, and the trucks were full of sacks, soft sacks covered with coal-dust. They were in fact bags filled with empty coal bags going back to their colliery. I crawled on top and burrowed in among them. In five minutes I was completely buried. The sacks were warm and comfortable. Perhaps the engine-driver had seen me rush up to the train and would give the alarm at the next station; on the other hand, perhaps not. Where was the train going to? Where would it be unloaded? Would it be searched? Was it on the Delagoa Bay line? What should I do in the morning? Ah, never mind that. Sufficient for the night was the luck thereof. Fresh plans for fresh contingencies. I resolved to sleep, nor can I imagine a more pleasing lullaby than the clatter of the train that carries an escaping prisoner at twenty miles an hour away from the enemy's capital.

"How long I slept I do not know, but I woke up suddenly with all feelings of exhilaration gone, and only the consciousness of oppressive difficulties heavy on me. I must leave the train before daybreak, so that I could drink at a pool and find some hiding-place while it was still dark. I would not run the risk of being unloaded with the coal bags. Another night I would board another train. I crawled from my cosy hiding-place among the sacks and sat again on the couplings. The train was running at a fair speed, but I felt it was time to leave it. I took hold of the iron handle at the back of the truck, pulled strongly with my left hand, and sprang. My feet struck the ground in two gigantic strides, and the next instant I was sprawling in the ditch considerably shaken but unhurt. The train, my faithful ally of the night, hurried on its journey.

"It was still dark. I was in the middle of a wide valley, surrounded by low hills, and carpeted with high grass drenched in dew. I searched for water in the nearest gully, and soon found a clear pool. I was very thirsty, but long after I had quenched my thirst I continued to drink, that I might have sufficient for the whole day.

"Presently the dawn began to break, and the sky to the east grew yellow and red, slashed across with heavy black clouds. I saw with relief that the railway ran steadily towards the sunrise. I had taken the right line, after all.

"Having drunk my fill, I set out for the hills, among which I hoped to find some hiding-place, and as it became broad daylight I entered a small grove of trees which grew on the side of a deep ravine. Here I resolved to wait till dusk. I had one consolation: no one in the world knew where I was—I did not know myself. It was now four o'clock. Fourteen hours lay between me and the night. My impatience to proceed while I was still strong doubled their length. At first it was terribly cold, but by degrees the sun gained power, and by ten o'clock the heat was oppressive. My sole companion was a gigantic vulture, who manifested an extravagant interest in my condition, and made hideous and ominous gurglings from time to time. From my lofty position I commanded a view of the whole valley. A little tin-roofed town lay three miles to the westward. Scattered farmsteads, each with a clump of trees, relieved the monotony of the undulating ground. At the foot of the hill stood a Kaffir kraal, and the figures of its inhabitants dotted the patches of cultivation or surrounded the droves of goats and cows which fed on the pasture. . . . During the day I ate one slab of chocolate, which, with the heat, produced a violent thirst. The pool was hardly half a mile away, but I dared not leave the shelter of the little wood, for I could see the figures of white men riding or walking occasionally across the valley, and once a Boer came and fired two shots at birds close to my hiding-place. But no one discovered me.

" The elation and the excitement of the previous night had burnt away, and a chilling reaction followed. I was very hungry, for I had had no dinner before starting, and chocolate, though it sustains, does not satisfy. I had scarcely slept, but yet my heart beat so fiercely and I was so nervous and perplexed about the future that I could not rest. I thought of all the chances that lay against me; I dreaded and detested more than words can express the prospect of being caught and dragged back to Pretoria. I found no comfort in any of the philosophical ideas which some men parade in their hours of ease and strength and safety. They seemed only fair-weather friends. I realized with awful force that no exercise of my own feeble wit and strength could save

54

me from my enemies, and that without the assistance of that High Power which interferes in the eternal sequence of causes and effects more often than we are always prone to admit, I could never succeed. I prayed long and earnestly for help and guidance. My prayer, as it seems to me, was swiftly and wonderfully answered."

I wrote these lines many years ago while the impression of adventure was strong upon me. Then I could tell no more. To have done so would have compromised the liberty and perhaps the lives of those who had helped me. For many years these reasons have disappeared. The time has come when I can relate the events which followed, and which changed my nearly hopeless position into one of superior advantage.

During the day I had watched the railway with attention. I saw two or three trains pass along it each way. I argued that the same number would pass at night. I resolved to board one of these. I thought I could improve on my procedure of the previous evening. I had observed how slowly the trains, particularly long goods trains, climbed some of the steep gradients. Sometimes they were hardly going at a foot's pace. It would probably be easy to choose a point where the line was not only on an up grade but also on a curve. Thus I could board some truck on the convex side of the train when both the engine and the guard's van were bent away, and when consequently neither the engine-driver nor the guard would see me. This plan seemed to me in every respect sound. I saw myself leaving the train again before dawn, having been carried forward another sixty or seventy miles during the night. That would be scarcely one hundred and fifty miles from the frontier.

And why should not the process be repeated? Where was the flaw? I could not see it. With three long bounds on three successive nights I could be in Portuguese territory. Meanwhile I still had two or three slabs of chocolate and a pocketful of crumbled biscuit— enough, that is to say, to keep body and soul together at a pinch without running the awful risk of recapture entailed by accosting a single human being. In this mood I watched with increasing impatience the arrival of darkness.

The long day reached its close at last. The western clouds flushed into fire; the shadows of the hills stretched out across the valley; a ponderous Boer wagon with its long team crawled slowly along the track towards the township, the Kaffirs collected their herds and drew them round their kraal; the daylight died, and soon it was quite dark. Then, and not until then, I set forth. I hurried to the railway line, scrambling along through the boulders and high grass and pausing on my way to drink at a stream of sweet cold water. I made my way to the place where I had seen the trains crawling so slowly up the slope, and soon found a point where the curve of the track fulfilled all the conditions of my plan. Here, behind a little bush, I sat down and waited hope-fully. An hour passed; two hours passed; three hours— and yet no train. Six hours had now elapsed since the last, whose time I had carefully noted, had gone by. Surely one was due. Another hour slipped away. Still no train! My plan began to crumble and my hopes to ooze out of me. After all, was it not quite possible that no trains ran on this part of the line during the dark hours? This was in fact the case, and I might well have con-tinued to wait in vain till daylight. However, between

twelve and one in the morning I lost patience and started
along the track, resolved to cover at any rate ten or
fifteen miles of my journey. I did not make much
progress. Every bridge was guarded by armed men;
every few miles were huts. At intervals there were
stations with tin-roofed villages clustering around them.
All the veldt was bathed in the bright rays of the full
moon, and to avoid these dangerous places I had to make
wide circuits and even to creep along the ground. Leaving the railroad I fell into bogs and swamps, brushed
through high grass dripping with dew, and waded across
the streams over which the bridges carried the railway.
I was soon drenched to the waist. I had been able to
take very little exercise during my month's imprison-
ment, and I was quickly tired with walking and with
want of food and sleep. Presently I approached a station.
It was a mere platform in the veldt, with two or three
buildings and huts around it. But laid up on the sidings,
obviously for the night, were three long goods trains.
Evidently the flow of traffic over the railway was uneven.
These three trains, motionless in the moonlight, con-
firmed my fears that traffic was not maintained by night
on this part of the line. Where, then, was my plan
which in the afternoon had looked so fine and sure?

It now occurred to me that I might board one of
these stationary trains immediately, and hiding amid its
freight be carried forward during the next day—and
night too if all were well. On the other hand, where
were they going to? Where would they stop? Where
would they be unloaded? Once I entered a wagon my
lot would be cast. I might find myself ignominiously
unloaded and recaptured at Witbank or Middelburg, or
at any station in the long two hundred miles which

separated me from the frontier. It was necessary at all costs before taking such a step to find out where these trains were going. To do this I must penetrate the station, examine the labels on the trucks or on the merchandise, and see if I could extract any certain guidance from them. I crept up to the platform and got between two of the long trains on the siding. I was proceeding to examine the markings on the trucks when loud voices rapidly approaching on the outside of the trains filled me with fear. Several Kaffirs were laughing and shouting in their unmodulated tones, and I heard, as I thought, a European voice arguing or ordering. At any rate, it was enough for me. I retreated between the two trains to the extreme end of the siding, and slipped stealthily but rapidly into the grass of the illimitable plain.

There was nothing for it but to plod on—but in an increasingly purposeless and hopeless manner. I felt very miserable when I looked around and saw here and there the lights of houses and thought of the warmth and comfort within them, but knew that they meant only danger to me. Far off on the moonlit horizon there presently began to shine the row of six or eight big lights which marked either Witbank or Middelburg station. Out in the darkness to my left gleamed two or three fires. I was sure they were not the lights of houses, but how far off they were or what they were I could not be certain. The idea formed in my mind that they were the fires of a Kaffir kraal. Then I began to think that the best use I could make of my remaining strength would be to go to these Kaffirs. I had heard that they hated the Boers and were friendly to the British. At any rate, they would probably not arrest me. They might give me food and a dry corner to sleep in. Although I could not speak a word of their language, yet I thought perhaps they might understand the value of a British banknote. They might even be induced to help me. A guide, a pony—but, above all, rest, warmth, and food—such were the promptings which dominated my mind. So I set out towards the fires.

I must have walked a mile or so in this resolve before a realization of its weakness and imprudence took possession of me. Then I turned back again to the railway line and retraced my steps perhaps half the distance. Then I stopped and sat down, completely baffled, destitute of any idea what to do or where to turn. Suddenly without the slightest reason all my doubts disappeared. It was certainly by no process of logic that they were dispelled. I just felt quite clear that I would go to the Kaffir kraal. I had sometimes in former years held a " Planchette " pencil and written while others had touched my wrist or hand. I acted in exactly the same unconscious or subconscious manner now.

I walked on rapidly towards the fires, which I had in the first instance thought were not more than a couple of miles from the railway line. I soon found they were much farther away than that. After about an hour or an hour and a half they still seemed almost as far off as ever. But I persevered, and presently between two and three o'clock in the morning I perceived that they were not the fires of a Kaffir kraal. The angular outline of buildings began to draw out against them, and soon I saw that I was approaching a group of houses around the mouth of a coal-mine. The wheel which worked the winding gear was plainly visible, and I could see that the fires which had led me so far were from the furnaces of the engines. Hard by, surrounded by one or two slighter structures, stood a small but substantial stone house two storeys high.

I halted in the wilderness to survey this scene and to revolve my action. It was still possible to turn back. But in that direction I saw nothing but the prospect of further futile wanderings terminated by hunger, fever, discovery, or surrender. On the other hand, here in front was a chance. I had heard it said before I escaped that in the mining district of Witbank and Middelburg there were a certain number of English residents who had been suffered to remain in the country in order to keep the mines working. Had I been led to one of these? What did this house which frowned dark and inscrutable upon me contain? A Briton or a Boer; a friend or a foe? Nor did this exhaust the possibilities. I had my seventy-five pounds in English notes in my pocket. If I revealed my identity, I thought that I could give reasonable assurance of a thousand. I might find some indifferent neutral-minded person who out of good nature or for a large sum of money would aid me in my bitter and desperate need. Certainly I would try to make what bargain I could now—now while I still had the strength to plead my cause and perhaps to extricate myself if the results were adverse. Still the odds were heavy against me, and it was with faltering and reluctant steps that I walked out of the shimmering gloom of the veldt into the light of the furnace fires, advanced towards the silent house, and struck with my fist upon the door.

There was a pause. Then I knocked again. And almost immediately a light sprang up above and an upper window opened.

" *Wer ist da?* " cried a man's voice.

I felt the shock of disappointment and consternation to my fingers.

"I want help; I have had an accident," I replied.

Some muttering followed. Then I heard steps descending the stairs, the bolt of the door was drawn, the lock was turned. It was opened abruptly, and in the darkness of the passage a tall man hastily attired, with a pale face and dark moustache, stood before me.

"What do you want?" he said, this time in English.

I had now to think of something to say. I wanted above all to get into parley with this man, to get matters in such a state that instead of raising an alarm and summoning others he would discuss things quietly.

"I am a burgher," I began. "I have had an accident. I was going to join my commando at Komati Poort. I have fallen off the train. We were skylarking. I have been unconscious for hours. I think I have dislocated my shoulder."

It is astonishing how one thinks of these things. This story leapt out as if I had learnt it by heart. Yet I had not the slightest idea what I was going to say or what the next sentence would be.

The stranger regarded me intently, and after some hesitation said at length, "Well, come in." He retreated a little into the darkness of the passage, threw open a door on one side of it, and pointed with his left hand into a dark room. I walked past him and entered, wondering if it was to be my prison. He followed, struck a light, lit a lamp, and set it on the table at the far side of which I stood. I was in a small room, evidently a dining-room and office in one. I noticed besides the large table, a roll desk, two or three chairs, and one of those machines for making soda-water, consisting of two glass globes set one above the other and encased in thin wire-netting. On his end of the table my host had laid a revolver, which he had hitherto presumably been holding in his right hand.

"I think I'd like to know a little more about this railway accident of yours," he said, after a considerable pause.

"I think," I replied, "I had better tell you the truth."

"I think you had," he said slowly.

So I took the plunge and threw all I had upon the board.

"I am Winston Churchill, War Correspondent of the *Morning Post*. I escaped last night from Pretoria. I am making my way to the frontier." (Making my way!) "I have plenty of money. Will you help me?"

There was another long pause. My companion rose from the table slowly and locked the door. After this act, which struck me as unpromising, and was certainly ambiguous, he advanced upon me and suddenly held out his hand.

"Thank God you have come here! It is the only house for twenty miles where you would not have been handed over. But we are all British here, and we will see you through."

It is easier to recall across the gulf of years the spasm of relief which swept over me, than it is to describe it. A moment before I had thought myself trapped; and now friends, food, resources, aid, were all at my disposal. I felt like a drowning man pulled out of the water and informed he has won the Derby!

WINSTON CHURCHILL—*My Early Life*.

WHALING

WHEN in the Southern Fishery, a captured Sperm Whale, after long and weary toil, is brought alongside late at night, it is not, as a general thing at least, customary to proceed at once to the business of cutting him in. For that business is an exceedingly laborious one; is not very soon completed; and requires all hands to set about it. Therefore, the common usage is to take in all sail; lash the helm a-lee; and then send everyone below to his hammock till daylight, with the reservation that, until that time, anchor-watches shall be kept; that is, two and two for an hour, each couple, the crew in rotation shall mount the deck to see that all goes well.

But sometimes, especially upon the Line in the Pacific, this plan will not answer at all; because such incalculable hosts of sharks gather round the moored carcase, that were he left so for six hours, say, on a stretch, little more than the skeleton would be visible by morning. In most other parts of the ocean, however, where these fish do not so largely abound, their wondrous voracity can be at times considerably diminished, by vigorously stirring them up with sharp whaling-spades, a procedure notwithstanding, which, in some instances, only seems to tickle them into still greater activity. But it was not thus in the present case with the *Pequod's* sharks; though, to be sure, any man unaccustomed to such sights, to have looked over her side that night, would have almost thought the whole round sea was one huge cheese, and those sharks the maggots in it.

Nevertheless, upon Stubb setting the anchor-watch after his supper was concluded; and when, accordingly, Queequeg and a forecastle seaman came on deck, no small excitement was created among the sharks; for immediately suspending the cutting stages over the side, and lowering three lanterns, so that they cast long gleams of light over the turbid sea, these two mariners, darting their long whaling-spades, kept up an incessant murdering of the sharks,[1] by striking the keen steel deep into their skulls, seemingly their only vital part. But in the foamy confusion of their mixed and struggling hosts, the marksmen could not always hit their mark; and this brought about new revelations of the incredible ferocity of the foe. They viciously snapped, not only at each other's disembowelments, but like flexible bows, bent round, and bit their own; till those entrails seemed swallowed over and over again by the same mouth, to be oppositely voided by the gaping wound. Nor was this all. It was unsafe to meddle with the corpses and ghosts of these creatures. A sort of generic or Pantheistic vitality seemed to lurk in their very joints and bones, after what might be called the individual life had departed. Killed and hoisted on deck for the sake of his skin, one of these sharks almost took poor Queequeg's

[1] The whaling-spade used for cutting-in is made of the very best steel; is about the bigness of a man's spread hand; and in general shape corresponds to the garden implement after which it is named; only its sides are perfectly flat, and its upper end considerably narrower than the lower. This weapon is always kept as sharp as possible; and when being used is occasionally honed, just like a razor. In its socket, a stiff pole, from twenty to thirty feet long, is inserted for a handle.

hand off, when he tried to shut down the dead lid of his murderous jaw.

It was a Saturday night, and such a Sabbath as followed! Ex-officio professors of Sabbath-breaking are all whalemen. The ivory *Pequod* was turned into what seemed a shamble; every sailor a butcher. You would have thought we were offering up ten thousand red oxen to the sea gods.

In the first place, the enormous cutting tackles, among other ponderous things comprising a cluster of blocks generally painted green, and which no single man can possibly lift—this vast bunch of grapes was swayed up to the maintop and firmly lashed to the lower masthead, the strongest point anywhere above a ship's deck. The end of the hawser-like rope winding through these intricacies, was then conducted to the windlass, and the huge lower block of the tackles was swung over the whale; to this block the great blubber hook, weighing some one hundred pounds, was attached. And now suspended in stages over the side, Starbuck and Stubb, the mates, armed with their long spades, began cutting a hole in the body for the insertion of the hook just above the nearest of the two side-fins. This done, a broad, semi-circular line is cut round the hole, the hook is inserted, and the main body of the crew striking up a wild chorus, now commence heaving in one dense crowd at the windlass. When instantly, the entire ship careens over on her side; every bolt in her starts like the nail-heads of an old house in frosty weather; she trembles, quivers, and nods her frighted mastheads to the sky. More and more she leans over to the whale, while every gasping heave of the windlass is answered by a helping heave from the billows; till at last, a swift, startling snap is heard; with a great swash the ship rolls upwards and backwards from the whale, and the triumphant tackle rises into sight dragging after it the disengaged semi-circular end of the first strip of blubber. Now as the blubber envelops the whale precisely as the rind does an orange, so is it stripped off from the body precisely as an orange is sometimes stripped by spiralizing it. For the strain constantly kept up by the windlass continually keeps the whale rolling over and over in the water, and as the blubber in one strip uniformly peels off along the line called the "scarf," simultaneously cut by the spades of Starbuck and Stubb, the mates; and just as fast as it is thus peeled off, and indeed by that very act itself, it is all the time being hoisted higher and higher aloft till its upper end grazes the maintop; the men at the windlass then cease heaving, and for a moment or two the prodigious blood-dripping mass sways to and fro as if let down from the sky, and everyone present must take good heed to dodge it when it swings, else it may box his ears and pitch him headlong overboard.

One of the attending harpooners now advances with a long, keen weapon called a boarding-sword, and watching his chance he dexterously slices out a considerable hole in the lower part of the swaying mass. Into this hole, the end of the second alternating great tackle is then hooked so as to retain a hold upon the blubber, in order to prepare for what follows. Whereupon, this accomplished swordsman, warning all hands to stand off, once more makes a scientific dash at the mass, and with a few sidelong, desperate, lunging slices, severs it completely in twain; so that while the short lower part is still fast, the long upper strip, called a blanket-piece, swings clear, and is all ready for lowering. The heavers forward now resume their song, and while the one tackle is peeling and hoisting a second strip from the whale, the other is slowly slackened away, and down goes the first strip through the main hatchway right beneath, into an unfurnished parlour called the blubber-room. Into this twilight apartment sundry nimble hands keep coiling away the long blanket-piece as if it were a great live mass of plaited serpents. And thus the work proceeds; the two tackles hoisting and lowering simultaneously; both whale and windlass heaving, the heavers singing, the blubber-room gentlemen coiling, the mates scarfing, the ship straining, and all hands swearing occasionally, by way of assuaging the general friction. . . .

A word or two more concerning this matter of the skin or blubber of the whale. It has already been said that it is stripped from him in long pieces, called blanket-pieces. Like most sea-terms, this one is very happy and significant. For the whale is indeed wrapped up in his blubber as in a real blanket or counterpane; or, still better, an Indian poncho slipped over his head, and skirting his extremity. It is by reason of this cosy blanketing of his body that the whale is enabled to keep himself comfortable in all weathers, in all seas, times, and tides. What would become of a Greenland whale, say, in those shuddering, icy seas of the North, if unsupplied with his cosy surtout? True, other fish are found exceedingly brisk in those Hyperborean waters; but these, be it observed, are your cold-blooded, lungless fish, whose very bellies are refrigerators; creatures that warm themselves under the lee of an iceberg, as a traveller in winter would bask before an inn fire; whereas, like man, the whale has lungs and warm blood.

Freeze his blood and he dies. How wonderful is it then —except after explanation—that this great monster, to whom corporeal warmth is as indispensable as it is to man; how wonderful that he should be found at home, immersed to his lips for life in those Arctic waters! where, when seamen fall overboard, they are sometimes found, months afterwards, perpendicularly frozen into the hearts of fields of ice, as a fly is found glued in amber. But more surprising is it to know, as has been proved by experiment, that the blood of a Polar whale is warmer than that of a Borneo negro in summer. . . .

"Haul in the chains! Let the carcase go astern!"

The vast tackles have now done their duty. The peeled white body of the beheaded whale flashes like a marble sepulchre; though changed in hue, it has not perceptibly lost anything in bulk. It is still colossal. Slowly it floats more and more away, the water round it torn and splashed by the insatiate sharks, and the air above vexed with rapacious flights of screaming fowls, whose beaks are like so many insulting poniards in the whale. The vast white headless phantom floats farther and farther from the ship, and every rod that it so floats, what seem square roods of sharks and cubic roods of fowls, augment the murderous din. For hours and hours from the almost stationary ship that hideous sight is seen. Beneath the unclouded and mild azure sky, upon the fair face of the pleasant sea, wafted by the joyous breezes, that great mass of death floats on and on, till lost in infinite perspectives.

There's a most doleful and most mocking funeral! The sea-vultures all in pious mourning, the air-sharks all punctiliously in black or speckled. In life but few of them would have helped the whale, I ween, if peradventure he had needed it; but upon the banquet of his funeral they most piously do pounce. Oh, horrible vulturism of earth! from which not the mightiest whale is free.

Nor is this the end. Desecrated as the body is, a vengeful ghost survives and hovers over it to scare. Espied by some timid man-of-war or blundering discovery-vessel from afar, when the distance obscuring the swarming fowls, nevertheless still shows the white mass floating in the sun, and the white spray heaving high against it; straightway the whale's unharming corpse, with trembling fingers is set down in the log—*shoals, rocks, and breakers hereabouts: beware!* And for years afterwards, perhaps, ships shun the place; leaping over it as silly sheep leap over a vacuum, because their leader originally leaped there when a stick was held. There's your law of precedents; there's your utility of traditions; there's the story of your obstinate survival of old beliefs never bottomed on the earth, and now not even hovering in the air!

Thus, while in life the great whale's body may have been a real terror to his foes, in his death his ghost becomes a powerful panic to the world.

HERMAN MELVILLE—*Moby Dick.*

THE CHINA TEA RACE

AT one that afternoon, as they passed Beachy all three ships began to feel the turn of the tide, the flying kites had to come in lest they should pitch the spars away. Then in little short spells of twenty minutes the wind would lull and the kites[1] would be set again; and in this kind of sailing Bloody Bill China had an advantage: as Cruiser could see, he had the boys aloft in the tops all the time ready to race up to loose the light sails or take them in. He was creeping up a little and a little, and was now only about a mile astern, having gained certainly a mile and a half in five hours. In another five hours the *Fu-Kien* would be half a mile ahead, having the pick of the tugs at the South Foreland. The *Caer Ocvran* was at a slight disadvantage, being not quite so happy in fresh or clearing weather as in light airs. However, her captain was fighting for every inch she lost. Cruiser with his small crew had only the miracle of the ship in his favour. He felt more and more keenly every instant that the ship was the best ship in the race. In other voyages she may not have been so: in this race all had conspired together, her builder and some happy combination in her trim, to make her supreme, but now she was short of hands, unable to do her best.

A darkness gathered into the heaven astern of them

[1] Light topmost sails.

as the secondary moved up. The hours of the afternoon dragged by as the ships strained up Channel, all drawing nearer, all watched by thousands ashore, who now guessed that those three moving beauties were the clippers of the China fleet.

Just off the Fairlight a little steamer, going with coals for Fowey, edged closer in to the *Bird of Dawning*, so as to have a good look at her. Cruiser hailed her through the trumpet.

"Ahoy, there, the *Chaffinch*, what China ship won the Race?"

"No ship," the *Chaffinch's* skipper shouted back. "You are the Race. Go in and win." . . .

The rain made a darkness about them for twenty minutes, during which Cruiser had two men on the fo'c's'le looking out.

As the squall cleared off, the sun drawing to the west shone out and made a rainbow upon its darkness. Under the arch of colours they saw the *Caer Ocvran* not two hundred yards from them on the starboard bow. She seemed to be stuck there in tossing waters that whitened about her in a great bubble.

Through the glass Cruiser could plainly see her captain, pacing his weather poop, glancing quickly aloft and at the *Bird of Dawning*. "Ah, yes, sir," Fairford said, as he watched, "you can glance and you can curse the helmsman, but the *Bird of Dawning's* got you beat to the wide."

"That's Captain Winstone," Cruiser said. "He was mate of the *Bidassoa* when I was in her. Look at that now: did you ever see a ship so wet?"

"She's famous for it, sir; the *Caer*. A fine ship, too."

Presently they were abreast of her, and forging ahead upon her, so that they could see her in her glory. She had a straight sheer and a transom stern,[1] having been built upon the lines of the famous French frigate, *L'Aigle*. In a light air no ship of her time could touch her, and she could run with the swiftest. She had a name through the seven seas for being wet: her decks now were running bright: for she was a caution in a head sea. They were watching and tending her now, getting some of her after-sail off her to keep her from burying her bow. Cruiser dipped his colours to her as he passed, but would not hail his old captain. As he drew clear, he saw her famous figurehead of Queen Gwenivere bowing down into the smother, then rising and pausing, then plunging down till the fo'c's'le-rail was lipping green.

"Look at that," Cruiser said. "Did you ever see a ship pitch like that?"

As he spoke, she took a deeper 'scend than usual, and rose with a snapped stunsail boom lifting on a loose wing.

The *Fu-Kien* drew clear of the *Caer Ocvran* on her lee-side: she was now a quarter of a mile away and gaining perhaps twenty yards a minute. Dungeness lay ahead, distant perhaps eight miles, and somewhere about Dungeness there would be pilots and perhaps tugs. There or thereabouts the race would be decided, another hour would see it out. Cruiser's men had been hard at it all day, and were showing signs of wear. They drank strong tea, syrupy with sugar and laced with brandy, as they got their hawsers ready forward and eyed the distant winning post.

[1] Shaped like the straight backboard of a boat.

All the issue from the gate of the Channel were about them: all the ships of a tide or two before from London and Antwerp, all the fishermen of Kent and Sussex. Every seaman who came past had no eyes for anything but those two superb clippers disputing for pride of place.

When the squall had passed by both had set every rag that could be brought to draw: they were now straining under clouds of canvas with a strong beam wind, and a head tide. Tarlton, who had been in the *Fu-Kien*, was not encouraging. "Just the wind she likes most," he said, "she's a glutton for it. And she laps up a head sea like a rum milk-punch." All the marvellous evening shone out mile after mile as they raced: the French coast plain as far as Calais, England white to windward, with occasional windows flashing like jewels, and a darkness of passing storm beyond. Occasional violent gusts kept men in both ships at the upper halliards; and still the *Fu-Kien* gained.

Cruiser was watching her now; she was not more than a hundred yards astern and to leeward, her decks full of men, and spare sails, all made up for bending, on each hatch, and the ship herself a picture of perfection, all bright for port, the paintwork and tarring finished; the hull black, with a white sheer-straik to set off her sheer, the yards black, man-of-war fashion, but with white yard-arms, and her masts all scraped clean with glass, of shining yellow pine. All her brass was bright, and the scroll below her bowsprit had been freshly gilt. She was driving on easily with great laughing leaps. Cruiser could see, in the bearing of the men in her, their certainty that they were winning. Both ships were hauling their wind now to turn the bend. Both could see now, coming out from Dungeness, the pilot cutter, standing towards them, not two miles away, and beyond, making for them what seemed to be tugs, but might be small coasters.

"Too bad, sir," old Fairford said. "We'd have done it if we'd had a bit more luck."

Cruiser was feeling broken-hearted at being passed on the post, but he could not take this view of it. "No, no," he said. "We've had such luck as no sailors ever had before. Think of what has come to us." All the same, he had to move away. When he was on the lee-poop staring at the *Fu-Kien*, old Fairford could not see how bitterly he felt.

As they hauled their wind, the *Fu-Kien* forged ahead upon them, standing close in upon them, intending to weather upon them and drive across their bows. Bloody Bill China was there on his poop, an unmistakable big figure with a hard tall grey hat jammed sideways on his head and a long pistol in his right hand. "That's Bloody Bill, sir," Tarlton said to Mr. Fairford. "Bloody Bill China, sir, the Captain. You'll see him send a bottle of brandy out to the yard-arm in a moment."

Sure enough a lad with a line went up the mizen-rigging and out to the crojick yard[1] with it, rove it through a jewel block at the yard-arm, and brought it down on deck. A bottle of brandy was hauled out to the yard-arm upon it and dangled there. "That's Bloody Bill's way, sir," Tarlton said. "If ever he weathers on a ship he shoots a bottle of brandy at the yard-arm and then splits another on all hands."

Twenty faces stared at the *Bird of Dawning* from the *Fu-Kien's* side. Those men of the sea, negroes, Malays

[1] The lowest yard on the mizen-mast.

and Europeans, grinned and cheered as their ship slid past.

Bloody Bill China, who was certainly half drunk, shouted something to his steward, who was standing near the break of the poop beside a grog-kid. The steward put a corkscrew into the cork of a bottle which he held. Bloody Bill strode to the ship's rail, and yelled at Cruiser, whom he took to be Captain Miserden, "Give my love to the Prophet Habakkuk."

Voices from the *Fu-Kien's* waist, eager for the promised grog, and full of joy in their victory, shouted "Habakkuk, Yah Yah, Habbakuk," and instantly the *Fu-Kien's* mainmast was ahead of the *Bird of Dawning's* mizen, and at once the *Fu-Kien's* crew manned the rail and cheered, and beat the fire signal on both her bells. Bloody Bill China brandished his pistol above his head, brought it down, and fired it as he fell: the bottle at the yard-arm was shattered—the brandy spilled. Instantly the steward drew his cork and Bloody Bill China shouted, "Grog-oh! The *Fu-Kien* wins the China Race."

She tore past the *Bird of Dawning*. She cleared her by a cable, then by three hundred yards. "Look out, sir," Tarlton cried to Cruiser. "He'll cross your bows as sure as God made Sunday."

And instantly Bloody Bill China did; he luffed up out of bravado, so as to get to windward of the *Bird of Dawning*.

He was going to cross her bows, just to show her. As he luffed, one of the violent gusts beat down upon both ships. Cruiser saw it coming and let go in time, but it caught the *Fu-Kien* fairly, and whipped her topgallant masts clean off in succession as one might count one, two, three. The great weight of gear swung to and fro on each mast, the fore-upper topsail went at the weather clue, the main-upper topsail halliards parted and the yard coming down brought the lower topsail with it, bending the truss and cockbilling[1] the yard. The helmsman let her go off, she fell off, thumping and thrashing while gear came flying down from the ruin. With a crash, the wreck of the foretopgallant mast, with its three yards, and stunsail booms and weight of sail and half a mile of rigging, collapsed about the forehatch.

It all had happened in a moment. Cruiser had been warned and had just time to heave the helm up. The *Bird of Dawning* always steered like a bird: she answered to a touch; she answered to it now, but the *Fu-Kien* was right athwart her hawse not three hundred yards away, falling off and coming down on her, with all the wreck on her mainmast visibly shaking the whole mast. One active daredevil soul was already racing with an axe to the splintered mast-head, to hack through the shrouds.

Cruiser saw her come round almost on her heel, straight at the *Bird of Dawning*. For about half a minute it seemed certain that the two would go into each other and sink each other. The mizen royal yard slid out of its bands and smote the *Fu-Kien's* deck end-on like a harpoon. The terrified helmsman hove the helm hard down; the ship, having still way on her, swung back into the wind; with a running, ripping, walloping crash, her main topgallant wreck came down into her waist, going through the bunt of the mainsail as it went.

The *Bird of Dawning* went past her and missed her by thirty yards. As they passed, Bloody Bill China leaped on to the top of the wheel-box, hurled his hard

[1] Pulling it askew.

hat at Cruiser, and while it was still in the air, settling to the sea, put three bullets through it with his pistol: he then hurled his pistol after it and leaped down cursing on to the main-deck to clear the wreck.

Cruiser left him to clear it; there, ranging down upon him, was the pilot cutter. In another minute that graceful boat rounded to with her pilot, who caught the tackle flung, and in an instant was swung high and brought upon the *Bird of Dawning's* deck.

The Pilot was a short man of enormous breadth, with a gentle manner. He seemed puzzled at the smallness of the crew and at the unusual untidiness of the deck, the planks not scrubbed nor oiled, the paint not freshened. He came up the weather ladder to Cruiser and shook him by the hand.

"I'm proud to welcome you, Captain," he said. "You're the first China clipper to take a pilot this year."

About five minutes later two tugs bore down upon them. Cruiser hoped as they drew near that they would be those telegraphed for by him. They were, however, two pirates, anxious to make the most of the situation. "Take you in, and dock you, for £100 a tug, Captain," their spokesman said.

"Are you the London and Dover Tug Company?"

"No, Captain; the South Foreland Tug Company. What about it?"

"Nothing doing."

"Now, Captain," the tugman cried. "You give us your line. £100 a tug is nothing to you if you win the prize. And with us you can't fail to win the prize. What's £100 a tug to honour and glory?"

"I'll give you £50 a tug," Cruiser said.

"Is that your last word?"

77

" Yes."

" Adew, my bucko," the tugman cried. Both tugs sheered off, in what Cruiser took to be the familiar gesture of a tugman driving a bargain. In this he was wrong, both tugs bore down on the *Fu-Kien* in such obvious distress astern. They had no doubt hoped that they might get a little salvage there. He saw them hang round the stern of the *Fu-Kien* while they drove their bargain and though Bill China was an ill man to bargain with, they drove it, for he saw them take position ahead to take the *Fu-Kien's* lines. But there was some little delay in their getting the lines, because the *Fu-Kien's* forward deck was a jumble of wreck not yet cleared. Old Fairford shook his head. " Ah, Captain Trews-bury," he said, " if you'll excuse my saying it, sir, ' Agree with thy adversary quickly' is wisdom when you're dealing with tugs. Now we're past the bend of the land this wind will fall and be tricky: we'll be as like as not becalmed before we're in the Downs: and there aren't too many tugs, sir. It'd be hard to see the *Fu-Kien* go past with those two fellows. Besides, sir, if the wind should fall light, as it will, we shall have the *Caer Ocvran* on us again. They say her captain can get way on her by blowing a flute on the poop."

" I dare say I was an ass," Cruiser said, " but we'll soon know."

There came a shout from forward on the starboard side. Efans came running aft.

" What's the matter? " Cruiser asked.

" The *Serica*, sir. She's peen on the French side, look you, and is standing ofer ahead of us."

" What of it? " Cruiser asked. " She can't sail against the wind."

78

He had watched that ship to leeward for some time, wondering if she could be one of the fleet. He had not thought her to be the *Serica*. If she were the *Serica*, then she, too, would be in the running, and might get a tug before him and beat them all. He looked at her through the telescope, and thought that she was liker the *Min and Win*; but a ship ahead of them by any name would be as ugly. "Well, I suppose I was an ass," he concluded to himself, as the evening closed in and the sun dipped into the clouds above England.

As old Fairford had foretold from the depth of his knowledge, the wind fell light and was tricky. Sheltered there in the Channel under the lee of the land, with the tide still ebbing, there was little lop on the water, which was of a dark grey now under the cliffs, and stretching green, with pinkish mottlings from the clouds, to distant France. Dover Pier and Castle and cliffs rose up: and there, bearing down upon him, were two tugs with tall scarlet smoke-stacks banded at the top with black. "There are the London and Dover tugs," he said.

"Them's them," old Fairford said. "The *Morning* and *Evening Star*." He sheered away to utter his real comment unheard: "And them two the *Fu-Kien's* got will eat the pair of them for breakfast."

As the *Evening Star* swung round, and came almost alongside, Cruiser saw his brother, the lawyer, standing on the bridge with the tug-captain.

"Hallo, Mike," he hailed. "How goes it?"

"Hallo, Cyril."

"You got my telegram?"

"Yes. I've settled with these tugs. I've settled everything."

"Give us your line, Captain," the tugman cried. The

lines were tossed down: in a few minutes the hawsers were passed and the tow to London River had begun.

Soon after they had started towing and before it had become too dark to see, the ship that men had thought to be the *Serica* showed clearly that she could not be the China clipper, but some unknown lofty ship bound for Dunkirk. Cruiser was able to judge the speed of the *Fu-Kien* under tow as less than his. He had a start of at least a couple of miles of her, and hoped to be able to maintain it.

In the last of the light he saw the *Caer Ocvran* come gliding up on a breath and signalling for steam. There was no tug for her. Presently the wind ceased, so that even the *Caer Ocvran* lay still in the calm.

The September night closed in upon them as they drew into the Downs. Deal lights twinkled to port; on ahead, on the starboard bow, the Gull Stream light gleamed out and vanished and again gleamed. Presently, as they finished with the sails and came from aloft in the dark, a big moon rose on the one hand, while on the other came the Kentish lights, Ramsgate Harbour and the North Foreland. A mile or two more brought them round the Elbow, into the great expanse starred with beacons, the Prince's Channel and the Girdler, with Shoebury far beyond. The night came cold and quiet, with a clear sky, into which the moon rose triumphing.

All through the night they towed, from the Channels to the Deeps and from the Deeps into the Reaches. The hard work of the voyage was over, but all hands stayed on deck ready for a call. Perrot made them suppers at odd times; some of them slept and others sang. Edgeworth stretched canvas over the ends of a cask and made a drum.

Before morning came, as Cruiser walked with the Pilot watching sleeping England and the unsleeping life of the river, a Kentish cock crowed for morning in some unseen roost. The faint magical noise reached the *Bird of Dawning*, and instantly her cock flapped on his perch in the coop and crowed in answer. Far away ashore on both sides of the river the cry passed from roost to roost. Cockcrow surely will rouse the dead at the dawn of judgment.

Soon light came into the sky: factory whistles blew to work, chimneys smoked; bells rang and the life of the port became busy about them. At eight o'clock, as they drew near to dock, a big steamer, coming down, beat her bells to them; her crowd of passengers, stewards and deckhands clustered at the rail and cheered them: she blew her siren, and passed them, dipping colours. Now down the river towards them came a flotilla of tugs, river-craft, skiffs, wherries and launches, all crowded, all gay with flags. The pierhead loomed up, black with people. The dockside railwaymen began to let off detonators. All those multitudes cheered and cheered, waved flags and streamers, flung their hats aloft and cried for the *Bird of Dawning*.

JOHN MASEFIELD—*The Bird of Dawning*

EAST, HALF SOUTH

On a day of high action in sea and sky we fled, hot-foot, before the fury of a nor'-west gale. We had run her overlong. Old Jock, for once at any rate, had had his weather eye bedimmed. He was expecting a quick shift into the sou'-west, a moderate gale, and a chance to make his "easting" round Cape Horn, but the wind hung stubbornly in the nor'-west; there was no break in the sky, no cessation in the black bursts of rain and sleet that swept upon us. A huge sea set up, and we were past the time when we could, in safety, heave her to the wind. There was nothing for it but to run—run she did.

We had tops'ls and a reefed foresail on her while day-light lasted, but on threat of darkness we stowed all but the foretops'l; wings enough for the weight of a hurri-cane wind. Under that narrow band of straining canvas she sped on into the murk of advancing night, while behind the lurid western sky showed threat of a mightier blast in bank upon bank of ragged storm-cloud. It was a wild night, never a wilder!

In the darkness the uncanny green shimmer of breaking seas gave an added terror to the scene of storm. Rain and stinging sleet swept constantly over us, thundering seas towered and curled at our stern, lapping viciously at the fleeting quarter, or, parting, crashed aboard at the waist, filling the decks man high with a power of destruction. Part of the bulwarks were torn from the side. That was, perhaps, the saving of us, for the seas swept off as fast as they thundered aboard, and the barque rode buoyant, when, with bulwarks standing, the weight of compassed water would have held her at mercy of the next towering greybeard. A boat on the forward skids was smashed to atoms and the wreck swept overboard, and every moment we looked to see our crazy half-deck go tottering to ruin. The fo'c's'le was awash through a shattered door, and all hands were gathered on the poop for such safety as it held. There was nowhere else where man could stand on the reeling hull, and crouching at the rails, wet and chilled to the marrow, we spent the night a-watching.

The bo'sun and Martin and Hans took turns of the steering; that was work beyond the rest of us, and the most we could do was to stand by a-lee and bear on the spokes with the helmsman. Dutchy was the best steersman, and his steering was no truer than the stout heart of him. Once she pooped, and the crest of a huge following sea came crashing on top of us. But for our hold-fasts, all would have been swept away. That was the time of trial. A falter at the helm—she would have "broached-to"—to utter destruction!

Amid the furious rush of broken water, "Dutchy" stood fast at his post, though there was a gash on his forehead and blood running in his eyes—the work of the wrenching wheel.

We showed no lights; no lamps would stand to the weather. There was only the flickering binnacle, tended as never was temple fire, to show the compass card. By turns we kept a look-out from the tops'l yard, but of what use was that when we could steer but to one point.

We were a ship of chance, and God help us and the out-ward-bounder, "hove-to" in the trough, that had come between us and the east that night!

How we looked for daylight! How it was long a-coming! How the mountain seas raced up and hove our barque, reeling from the blow, from towering crest to hollow of the trough! How every day of the twenty-five years of her cried out in creak of block, in clatter of chain sheet, in the "harping" of the backstays, the straining groan of the burdened masts!

From time to time through the night the Mate and some of us would go forward to see to the gear; there was no need to touch a brace, for the wind blew omin-ously true. When we got back again, battered and breathless, it was something to know that the foretops'l still stood the strain. It was a famous sail, a web of "00 storm," stitched and fortified at seam and roping for such a wind as this. Good luck to the hands that stitched it, to the dingy sail loft in the Govan Road that turned it out, for it stood us in stead that night!

Once an ill-stowed clew of the mains'l blew out with a sounding crack, and thrashed a "devil's tattoo" on the yard. We thought it the tops'l gone—but no! Macallison's best stood bravely spread to the shrieking gale, and we soon had the ribbons of the main clew fast to the yard.

There was no broad dawn, no glow in the east to mark its breaking; the light grew out of the darkness. The masts and spars shaped themselves out of the gloom, till they stood outlined against the dull grey clouds. We could see the great seas, white-streaked by lash of driven spray, running up into the lowering sky. When day came, and the heaving, wind-swept face of the waters became plain to us, we saw the stormy path round the Horn in its wildest, grandest mood. Stretching far to the black murky curtain—the rear of the last shrieking rain squall—the great Cape Horn greybeards swept on with terrific force and grandeur, their mile-long crests hurtling skyward in blinding foam. The old barque ran well, reeling through the long, stormy slopes with buoyant spring, driving wildly to the trough, smashing the foam far aside. At times she poised with sickening uncertitude on the crest of a greater wave, then steadied, and leapt with the breaking water to the smoother hollow.

The Old Man stood by the helmsman, "conning" her on. All night he had stood there, ordering, to the shock of following seas, a steady voiced command. Never a gainly man—short-legged, broad, uncouth—his was yet a figure in keeping with the scene; unkempt and haggard, blue-lipped, drenched by sea and rain, he was never less than a Master of the Sea. At daybreak we heard a hail from the tops'l yard, and saw the "look-out" pointing ahead. Peering down the wind, we made out the loom of a ship rising and falling in the trough of the sea. A big "four-master" she proved, lying "hove-to" the wind. We shuddered to think of what would have been if daylight had been further delayed!

Out of the mist and spray we bore down on her and flew by, close to her stern. We could see figures on her poop staring and pointing, a man with glasses at his eyes. Only a fleeting glimpse—for she was soon swallowed up by the murk astern, and we were driving on. The shift of wind came suddenly. Nearly at noon there was a heavier fall of rain, a shrieking squall that blew as it had never blown. The Old Man marked the signs

—the scud of the upper clouds, a brightening low down in the south.

" Stan' by . . . head . . . yards," he yelled, shouting hoarsely to be heard. " Quick . . . the word! "

All hands struggled to the braces, battling through the wash of icy water that swept over the decks.

The squall passed, followed by a lull that served us to cant the yards; then, sharp as a knife-thrust, the wind came howling out of the sou'-west. The rain ceased and the sky cleared as by a miracle. Still it blew and the seas, turned by the shift of wind, broke and shattered in a whirl of confusion. For a time we laboured through the treacherous cross sea—the barque fretting and turning to windward, calling for all of " Dutchy's " cunning at the helm, but it was none so ill with the sun in sight and a clearing overhead.

" Blast ye," said the Old Man, shaking his benumbed arms towards the sou'-west. " Blast ye—but ye've been a long time comin'! "

The wind was now to his liking, it was the weather he had looked for, and sure enough, as quick succeeding squalls rolled up on us, the sea grew less and ran truer, and the barque sailed easier. The wind fell to a moderate gale, and by four in the afternoon we had a reefed foresail and the tops'ls set, and were staggering along at a great speed.

The decks were yet awash, there was no comfort on deck or below; but through it all we had one consoling thought: *East, half south*, we were covering the leagues that lay between us and our journey's end!

DAVID W. BONE—*The Brassbounder.*

FOUR JOVIAL SPORTSMEN

Pisc. Well met, brother Peter: I heard you and a friend would lodge here to-night, and that hath made me to bring my friend to lodge here too. My friend is one that would fain be a brother of the angle; he hath been an angler but this day, and I have taught him how to catch a chub by dapping with a grasshopper, and the chub that he caught was a lusty one of nineteen inches long. But pray, brother Peter, who is your companion?

Peter. Brother Piscator, my friend is an honest countryman, and his name is Coridon, and he is a downright witty companion, that met me here purposely to be pleasant and eat a trout; and I have not yet wetted my line since we met together; but I hope to fit him with a trout for his breakfast, for I'll be early up.

Pisc. Nay, brother, you shall not stay so long: for, look you, here is a trout will fill six reasonable bellies.

Come, hostess, dress it presently, and get us what other meat the house will afford, and give us some of your best barley-wine, the good liquor that our honest forefathers did use to drink of; the drink which preserved their health, and made them live so long, and to do so many good deeds.

Peter. On my word, this TROUT is perfect in season. Come, I thank you, and here is a hearty draught to you, and to all the brothers of the angle wheresoever they be, and to my young brother's good fortune to-morrow. I will furnish him with a rod if you will furnish him with the rest of the tackling; we will set him up and make him a fisher. And I will tell him one thing for his encouragement, that his fortune hath made him happy to be scholar to such a master; a master that knows as much, both of the nature and breeding of fish, as any man; and can also tell him as well how to catch and cook them, from the minnow to the salmon, as any that I ever met withal.

Pisc. Trust me, brother Peter, I find my scholar to be so suitable to my own humour, which is, to be free and pleasant and civilly merry, that my resolution is to hide nothing that I know from him. Believe me, scholar, this is my resolution; and so here's to you a hearty draught, and to all that love us and the honest art of angling.

Ven. Trust me, good master, you shall not sow your seed in barren ground; for I hope to return you an increase answerable to your hopes: but, however, you shall find me obedient and thankful, and serviceable to my best ability.

Pisc. 'Tis enough, honest scholar! come, let's to supper. Come, my friend Coridon, this trout looks lovely; it was twenty-two inches when it was taken; and the belly of it looked, some part of it, as yellow as a marigold, and part of it as white as a lily; and yet, methinks, it looks better in this good sauce.

Coridon. Indeed, honest friend, it looks well, and tastes well: I thank you for it, and so doth my friend Peter, or else he is to blame.

Peter. Yes, and so I do, we all thank you; and when we have supped, I will get my friend Coridon to sing you a song for requital.

Cor. I will sing a song, if anybody will sing another; else, to be plain with you, I will sing none. I am none of those that sing for meat, but for company: I say,

> 'Tis merry in hall,
> When men sing all.

Pisc. I'll promise you I'll sing a song that was lately made, at my request, by Mr. William Basse, one that hath made the choice songs of the "Hunter in his career," and of "Tom of Bedlam," and many others of note; and this that I will sing, is in praise of angling.

Cor. And then mine shall be the praise of a country-man's life: what will the rest sing of?

Peter. I will promise you, I will sing another song in praise of angling to-morrow night; for we will not part till then, but fish to-morrow, and sup together, and the next day every man leave fishing, and fall to his business.

Ven. 'Tis a match; and I will provide you a song or a catch against then, too, which shall give some addition of mirth to the company; for we will be civil and as merry as beggars.

Pisc. 'Tis a match, my masters; let's e'en say grace, and turn to the fire, drink the other cup to whet our whistles, and so sing away all sad thoughts.

IZAAK WALTON—*The Compleat Angler.*

THE ADDER'S STING

In the evening he set out on the journey. Although the heat of summer was yet intense the days had considerably shortened, and before he had advanced a mile on his way all the heath purples, browns, and greens had merged in a uniform dress without airiness or gradation, and broken only by touches of white where the little heaps of clean quartz sand showed the entrance to a rabbit-burrow, or where the white flints of a footpath lay like a thread over the slopes. In almost every one of the isolated and stunted thorns which grew here and there a night-hawk revealed his presence by whirring like the clack of a mill as long as he could hold his breath, then stopping, flapping his wings, wheeling round the bush, alighting, and after a silent interval of listening beginning to whir again. At each brushing of Clym's feet white miller-moths flew into the air just high enough to catch upon their dusty wings the mellowed light from the west, which now shone across the depressions and levels of the ground without falling thereon to light them up.

Yeobright walked on amid this quiet scene with a hope that all would soon be well. Three miles on he came to a spot where a soft perfume was wafted across his path, and he stood still for a moment to inhale the familiar scent. It was the place at which, four hours earlier, his mother had sat down exhausted on the knoll covered with shepherd's-thyme. While he stood a sound between a breathing and a moan suddenly reached his ears.

He looked to where the sound came from; but nothing appeared there save the verge of the hillock stretching against the sky in an unbroken line. He moved a few steps in that direction, and now he perceived a recumbent figure almost close at his feet.

Among the different possibilities as to the person's individuality there did not for a moment occur to Yeobright that it might be one of his own family. Sometimes furze-cutters had been known to sleep out of doors at these times, to save a long journey homeward and back again; but Clym remembered the moan and looked closer, and saw that the form was feminine; and a distress came over him like cold air from a cave. But he was not absolutely certain that the woman was his mother till he stooped and beheld her face, pallid, and with closed eyes.

His breath went, as it were, out of his body and the cry of anguish which would have escaped him died upon his lips. During the momentary interval that elapsed before he became conscious that something must be done all sense of time and place left him, and it seemed as if he and his mother were as when he was a child with her many years ago on this heath at hours similar to the present. Then he awoke to activity; and bending yet lower he found that she still breathed, and that her breath though feeble was regular, except when disturbed by an occasional gasp.

"Oh, what is it! Mother, are you very ill—you are not dying?" he cried, pressing his lips to her face. "I am your Clym. How did you come here? What does it all mean? "

At that moment the chasm in their lives which his love for Eustacia had caused was not remembered by Yeobright, and to him the present joined continuously with that friendly past that had been their experience before the division.

She moved her lips, appeared to know him, but could not speak; and then Clym strove to consider how best to move her, as it would be necessary to get her away from the spot before the dews were intense. He was able-bodied, and his mother was thin. He clasped his arms round her, lifted her a little, and said, "Does that hurt you? "

She shook her head, and he lifted her up; then, at a slow pace, went onward with his load. The air was now completely cool; but whenever he passed over a sandy patch of ground uncarpeted with vegetation there was reflected from its surface into his face the heat which it had imbibed during the day. At the beginning of his undertaking he had thought but little of the distance which yet would have to be traversed before Blooms-End could be reached; but though he had slept that afternoon he soon began to feel the weight of his burden. Thus he proceeded, like Æneas with his father; the bats circling round his head, nightjars flapping their wings within a yard of his face, and not a human being within call.

While he was yet nearly a mile from the house his mother exhibited signs of restlessness under the constraint of being borne along, as if his arms were irksome to her. He lowered her upon his knees and looked around. The point they had now reached, though far from any road, was not more than a mile from the Blooms-End cottages occupied by Fairway, Sam, Humphrey, and the Cantles. Moreover, fifty yards off stood a hut, built of clods and covered with thin turves, but now entirely disused. The simple outline of the lonely shed was visible, and thither he determined to direct his steps. As soon as he arrived he laid her down carefully by the entrance, and then ran and cut with his pocket-knife an armful of the driest fern. Spreading this within the shed, which was entirely open on one side, he placed his mother thereon: then he ran with all his might towards the dwelling of Fairway.

Nearly a quarter of an hour had passed, disturbed only by the broken breathing of the sufferer, when moving figures began to animate the line between heath and sky. In a few moments Clym arrived with Fairway, Humphrey, and Susan Nunsuch; Olly Dowden, who had chanced to be at Fairway's, Christian and Grandfer Cantle following helter-skelter behind. They had brought a lantern and matches, water, a pillow, and a few other articles which had occurred to their minds in the hurry of the moment. Sam had been dispatched back again for brandy, and a boy brought Fairway's pony, upon which he rode off to the nearest medical man, with directions to call at Wildeve's on his way, and inform Thomasin that her aunt was unwell.

Sam and the brandy soon arrived, and it was administered by the light of the lantern; after which she became sufficiently conscious to signify by signs that something was wrong with her foot. Olly Dowden at length understood her meaning, and examined the foot indicated. It was swollen and red. Even as they watched the red began to assume a more livid colour, in the midst of which appeared a scarlet speck, smaller than a pea, and it was found to consist of a drop of blood, which rose above the smooth flesh of her ankle in a hemisphere.

"I know what it is," cried Sam. "She has been stung by an adder!"

"Yes," said Clym instantly. "I remember when I was a child seeing just such a bite. Oh, my poor mother!"

"It was my father who was bit," said Sam. "And there's only one way to cure it. You must rub the place with the fat of other adders, and the only way to get that is by frying them. That's what they did for him."

"'Tis an old remedy," said Clym distrustfully, "and I have doubts about it. But we can do nothing else till the doctor comes."

"'Tis a sure cure," said Olly Dowden, with emphasis. "I've used it when I used to go out nursing."

"Then we must pray for daylight, to catch them," said Clym gloomily.

"I will see what I can do," said Sam.

He took a green hazel which he had used as a walking-stick, split it at the end, inserted a small pebble, and with the lantern in his hand went out into the heath. Clym had by this time lit a small fire, and dispatched Susan Nunsuch for a frying-pan. Before she had returned Sam came in with three adders, one briskly coiling and uncoiling in the cleft of the stick, and the other two hanging dead across it.

"I have only been able to get one alive and fresh as he ought to be," said Sam. "These limp ones are two I killed to-day at work; but as they don't die till the sun goes down they can't be very stale meat."

The live adder regarded the assembled group with a

sinister look in its small black eye, and the beautiful brown and jet pattern on its back seemed to intensify with indignation. Mrs. Yeobright saw the creature, and the creature saw her: she quivered throughout, and averted her eyes.

"Look at that," murmured Christian Cantle. "Neighbours, how do we know but that something of the old serpent in God's garden, that gied the apple to the young woman with no clothes, lives on in adders and snakes still? Look at his eye—for all the world like a villainous sort of black currant. 'Tis to be hoped he can't ill-wish us! There's folks in heath who've been overlooked already. I will never kill another adder as long as I live."

"Well, 'tis right to be afeard of things, if folks can't help it," said Grandfer Cantle. "'Twould have saved me many a brave danger in my time."

"I fancy I heard something outside the shed," said Christian. "I wish troubles would come in the daytime, for then a man could show his courage, and hardly beg for mercy of the most broomstick old woman he should see, if he was a brave man, and able to run out of her sight!"

"Even such an ignorant fellow as I should know better than do that," said Sam.

"Well, there's calamities where we least expect it, whether or no. Neighbours, if Mrs. Yeobright were to die, d'ye think we should be took up and tried for the manslaughter of a woman?"

"No, they couldn't bring it in as that," said Sam, "unless they could prove we had been poachers at some time of our lives. But she'll fetch round."

"Now, if I had been stung by ten adders I should hardly have lost a day's work for't," said Grandfer

Cantle. "Such is my spirit when I am on my mettle. But perhaps 'tis natural in a man trained for war. Yes, I've gone through a good deal; but nothing ever came amiss to me after I joined the Locals in four." He shook his head and smiled at a mental picture of himself in uniform. "I was always first in the most galliantest scrapes in my younger days! "

"I suppose that was because they always used to put the biggest fool afore," said Fairway from the fire, beside which he knelt, blowing it with his breath.

"D'ye think so, Timothy? " said Grandfer Cantle, coming forward to Fairway's side with sudden depression in his face. "Then a man may feel for years that he is good solid company, and be wrong about himself after all? "

"Never mind that question, Grandfer. Stir your stumps and get some more sticks. 'Tis very nonsense of an old man to prattle so when life and death's in mangling."

"Yes, yes," said Grandfer Cantle, with melancholy conviction. "Well, this is a bad night altogether for them that have done well in their time; and if I were ever such a dab at the hautboy or tenor-viol, I shouldn't have the heart to play tunes upon 'em now."

Susan now arrived with the frying-pan, when the live adder was killed and the heads of the three taken off. The remainders, being cut into lengths and split open, were tossed into the pan, which began hissing and crackling over the fire. Soon a rill of clear oil trickled from the carcases, whereupon Clym dipped the corner of his handkerchief into the liquid and anointed the wound.

THOMAS HARDY—*The Return of the Native.*

NOTHING BUT THE TRUTH

When evening came we were all wide awake and sat till a very late hour round the fire we had made in the hollow, sipping maté and conversing. We were all in a talkative mood that evening, and after the ordinary subjects of Banda Orientál conversation had been exhausted, we drifted into matters extraordinary—wild creatures of strange appearance and habits, apparitions, and marvellous adventures.

"The manner in which the lampalagua captures its prey is very curious," said one of the company, named Rivarola, a stout man with an immense fierce-looking black beard and moustache, but who was very mild-eyed and had a gentle, cooing voice.

We had all heard of the lampalagua, a species of boa found in these countries, with a very thick body and extremely sluggish in its motions. It preys on the larger rodents, and captures them, I believe, by following them into their burrows, where they cannot escape from its jaws by running.

"I will tell you what I once witnessed, for I have never seen a stranger thing," continued Rivarola. "Riding one day through a forest I saw some distance before me a fox sitting on the grass watching my approach. Suddenly I saw it spring high up into the air, uttering a great scream of terror, then fall back upon the earth, where it lay for some time growling, struggling, and biting as if engaged in deadly conflict with some invisible enemy. Presently it began to move away through the wood, but very slowly and still frantically struggling. It seemed to be getting exhausted, its tail dragged, the mouth foamed, and the tongue hung out, while it still moved on as if drawn by an unseen cord. I followed, going very close to it, but it took no notice of me. Sometimes it dug its claws into the ground or seized a twig or stalk with its teeth, and it would then remain resting for a few moments till the twig gave away, when it would roll over many times on the ground, loudly yelping, but still dragged onwards. Presently I saw in the direction we were going a huge serpent, thick as a man's thigh, its head lifted high above the grass, and motionless as a serpent of stone. Its cavernous, blood-red mouth was gaping wide, and its eyes were fixed on the struggling fox. When about twenty yards from the serpent, the fox began moving very rapidly over the ground, its struggles growing feebler every moment, until it seemed to fly through the air, and in an instant was in the serpent's mouth. Then the reptile dropped its head and began slowly swallowing its prey."

"And you actually witnessed this yourself?" said I.

"With these eyes," he returned, indicating the orbs in question by pointing at them with the tube of the maté-cup he held in his hand. "This was the only occasion on which I have actually seen the lampalagua take its prey, but its manner of doing it is well known to everyone from hearsay. You see, it draws an animal towards it by means of its power of suction. Sometimes, when the animal attacked is very strong or very far off—say two thousand yards—the serpent becomes so inflated with the quantity of air inhaled while drawing the victim towards it——"

"That it bursts?" I suggested.

"That it is obliged to stop drawing to blow the wind out. When this happens, the animal, finding itself released from the drawing force, instantly sets off at full speed. Vain effort! The serpent has no sooner discharged the accumulated wind with a report like a cannon——"

"No, no, like a musket! I have heard it myself," interrupted Blas Aria, one of the listeners.

"Like a musket, than it once more brings its power of suction to bear; and in this manner the contest continues until the victim is finally drawn into the monster's jaws. It is well known that the lampalagua is the strongest of all God's creatures, and that if a man, stripped to the skin, engages one, and conquers it by sheer muscular strength, the serpent's power goes into him, after which he is invincible."

I laughed at this fable, and was severely rebuked for my levity.

"I will tell you the strangest thing that ever befell me," said Blas Aria. "I happened to be travelling alone —for reasons—on the northern frontier. I crossed the river Yaguaron into Brazilian territory, and for a whole day rode through a great marshy plain, where the reeds were dead and yellow, and the water shrunk into muddy pools. It was a place to make a man grow weary of life. When the sun was going down, and I began to despair of getting to the end of this desolation, I discovered a low hovel made of mud and thatched with rushes. It was about fifteen yards long, with only one small door, and seemed to be uninhabited, for no person answered me when I rode round it shouting aloud. I heard a grunting and squealing within, and by and by a sow, followed by a litter of young pigs, came out, looked at me, then went in again. I would have ridden on, but my horses were tired; besides, a great storm with thunder and lightning was coming up, and no other shelter appeared in sight. I therefore unsaddled, loosed my horses to feed, and took my gear into the hovel. The room I entered was so small that the sow and her young occupied all the floor; there was, however, another room, and opening the door, which was closed, I went into it and found that it was very much larger than the first; also, that it contained a dirty bed made of skins in one corner, while on the floor was a heap of ashes and a black pot. There was nothing else except old bones, sticks, and other rubbish littering the floor. Afraid of being caught unawares by the owner of this foul den, and finding nothing to eat in it, I returned to the first room, turned the pigs out of doors, and sat down on my saddle to wait. It was beginning to get dark when a woman, bringing in a bundle of sticks, suddenly appeared at the door. Never, sirs, have I beheld a fouler, more hideous object than this person. Her face was hard, dark, and rough like the bark of the ñandubuy tree, while her hair, which covered her head and shoulders in a tangled mass, was of a dry earthy colour. Her body was thick and long, yet she looked like a dwarf, for she scarcely had any legs, only enormous knees and feet; and her garments were old ragged horse-rugs tied round her body with thongs of hide. She stared at me out of a pair of small black rat eyes, then, setting down her bundle, asked me what I wanted. I told her I was a tired traveller, and wanted food and shelter. 'Shelter you can have: food there is none,' she said; then, taking up her sticks, she passed to the inner room and secured it with a bolt on the inside. She had not inspired me with love, and there was little danger of my attempting to intrude on her there. It was a black, stormy night, and very soon the rain began to fall in torrents. Several times the sow, with her young pigs loudly squealing, came in for shelter, and I was forced to get up and beat them out with my whip. At length, through the mud partition separating the two rooms, I heard the crackling of a fire which the vile woman was lighting; and, before long, through the chinks came the savoury smell of roast meat. That surprised me greatly, for I had searched the room and failed to find anything to eat in it. I concluded that she had brought in the meat under her garments, but where she had got it was a mystery. At length I began to doze. There were many sounds in my ear as of thunder and wind, the pigs grunting at the door, and the crackling of the fire in the hag's room. But by and by other sounds seemed to mingle with these—voices of several persons talking, laughing, and singing. At length I became wide awake, and found that these voices proceeded from the next room. Some person was playing a guitar and singing, then others were loudly talking and laughing. I tried to peep through the cracks in the door and partition, but could not see through them. High up in the middle of the wall there was one large crack through which I was sure the interior could be seen, so much red firelight streamed through it. I placed my saddle against the partition, and all my rugs folded small, one above the other, until I had heaped them as high as my knees. Standing on my toes on this pile, and carefully clinging to the wall with my fingernails, I managed to bring my eyes to a level with the crack, and peeped through it. The room inside was brightly lighted by a big wood fire burning at one end, while on the floor a large crimson cloak was spread, on which the people I had heard were sitting with some fruit and bottles of wine before them. There was the foul hag looking almost as tall sitting as she had appeared when standing; she was playing on a guitar and singing a ballad in Portuguese. Before her on the cloak lay a tall well-formed negro woman, wearing only a narrow white cloth round her loins, and broad silver armlets on her round black arms. She was eating a banana, and against her knees, which were drawn up, sat a beautiful girl about fifteen years old, with a dark pale face. She was dressed in white, her arms were bare, and round her head she wore a gold band keeping back her black hair, which fell unbound on her back. Before her, on his knees on the cloak, was an old man with a face brown and wrinkled as a walnut, and beard white as thistledown. With one of his hands he was holding the girl's arm, and with the other offering her a glass of wine. All this I saw at one glance, and then all of them together turned their eyes up at the crack as if they knew that someone was watching them. I started back in alarm, and fell with a crash to the ground. Then I heard loud screams of laughter, but I dared not attempt to look in on them again. I took my rugs to the farther side of the room, and sat down to wait for morning. The talking and laughter continued for about two hours, then it gradually died away, the light faded from the chinks, and all was dark and silent. No person came out; and at last, overcome with drowsiness, I fell asleep. It was day when I woke. I rose and walked round the hovel, and finding a crack in the wall, I peered into the hag's room. It looked just as I had seen it the day before; there was the pot and pile of ashes, and in the corner the brutish woman lying asleep in her skins. After that I got on to my horse and rode away. May I never again have such an experience as I had that night."

Something was then said about witchcraft by the others, all looking very solemn.

"You were very hungry and tired that night," I ventured to remark, "and perhaps after the woman locked her door you went to sleep and dreamed all that about people eating fruit and playing on the guitar."

"Our horses were tired and we were flying for our lives yesterday," returned Blas contemptuously. "Perhaps it made us dream that we caught five dun horses to carry us." . . .

Lechuza sat inattentive, smoking his cigarette, and when we had all done speaking began:

"I once had an encounter with a strange being. I was a young man then—young and full of the fire, strength and courage of youth—for what I am now going to relate happened over twenty years ago. I had been playing cards at a friend's house, and left it at midnight to ride to my father's house, a distance of five leagues. I had quarrelled that evening and left a loser, burning with anger against the man who had cheated and insulted me, and with whom I was not allowed to fight. Vowing vengeance on him, I rode away at a fast gallop; the night being serene, and almost as light as day, for the moon was at its full. Suddenly I saw before me a huge man sitting on a white horse, which stood perfectly motionless directly in my path. I dashed on till I came near him, then shouted aloud, ' Out of my path, friend, lest I ride over you '; for I was still raging in my heart.

" Seeing that he took no notice of my words, I dug my spurs into my horse and hurled myself against him; then at the very moment my horse struck his with a tremendous shock, I brought down my iron whip-handle with all the force that was in me upon his head. The blow rang as if I had struck upon an anvil, while at the same moment he, without swerving, clutched my cloak with both hands. I could feel that they were bony, hard hands, armed with long, crooked, sharp talons like an eagle's, which pierced through my cloak into my flesh. Dropping my whip, I seized him by the throat, which seemed scaly and hard, between my hands, and thus, locked together in a desperate struggle, we swayed this way and that, each trying to drag the other from his seat till we came down together with a crash upon the earth. In a moment we were disengaged and on our feet. Quick as lightning flashed out his long, sharp weapon, and finding I was too late to draw mine I hurled myself against him, seizing his armed hand in both mine before he could strike. For a few moments he stood still, glaring at me out of a pair of eyes that shone like burning coals; then mad with rage, he flung me off my feet and whirled me round and round like a ball in a sling, and finally cast me from him to a distance of a hundred yards, so great was his strength. I was launched with tremendous force into the middle of some thorny bushes, but had no sooner recovered from the shock than out I burst with a yell of rage and charged him again. For, you will hardly believe it, sirs, by some strange chance I had carried away his weapon, firmly grasped in my hands. It was a heavy two-edged dagger, sharp as a needle, and while I grasped the hilt I felt the strength and fury of a thousand fighting-men in me. As I advanced he retreated before me, until, seizing the topmost boughs of a great thorny bush he swung his body to one side and wrenched it out of the earth by the roots. Swinging the bush with the rapidity of a whirlwind round his head, he advanced against me and dealt a blow that would have crushed me had it descended on me; but it fell too far, for I had dodged under it to close with him and delivered a stab with such power that the long weapon was buried to its hilt in his bosom. He uttered a deafening yell, and at the same moment a torrent of blood spouted forth, scalding my face like boiling water, and drenching my clothes through to the skin. For a moment I was blinded; but when I had dashed the blood from my eyes and looked round he had vanished, horse and all.

"Then mounting my horse I rode home and told everyone what had happened, showing the knife, which I still carried in my hand. Next day all the neighbours gathered at my house, and we rode in company to the spot where the fight had taken place. There we found the bush torn up by the roots, and all the earth about it ploughed up where we had fought. The ground was also dyed with blood for several yards round, and where it had fallen the grass was withered up to the roots, as if scorched with fire. We also picked up a cluster of hairs—long, wiry, crooked hairs, barbed at the ends like fish-hooks; also three or four scales like fish-scales, only rougher, and as large as doubloons. The spot where the fight took place is now called *La Cañada del Diablo*, and I have heard that since that day the devil has never

appeared corporeally to fight any man in the Banda
Orientál."

Lechuza's narrative gave great satisfaction. I said
nothing, feeling half stupid with amazement, for the
man apparently told it in the full conviction that it was
true, while the other listeners appeared to accept every
word of it with the most implicit faith. I began to feel
very melancholy, for evidently they expected something
from me now, and what to tell them I knew not. It
went against my conscience to be the only liar amongst
these exceedingly veracious Orientals, and so I could not
think of inventing anything.

"My friends," I began at length, "I am only a young
man; also a native of a country where marvellous things
do not often happen, so that I can tell you nothing to
equal in interest the stories I have heard. I can only
relate a little incident which happened to me in my own
country before I left it. It is trivial, perhaps, but will
lead me to tell you something about London—that great
city you have all heard of."

"Yes, we have heard of London; it is in England, I
believe. Tell us your story about London," said Blas
encouragingly.

"I was very young—only fourteen years old," I continued, flattering myself that my modest introduction
had not been ineffective, "when one evening I came to
London from my home. It was in January, in the middle
of winter, and the whole country was white with
snow."

"Pardon me, Captain," said Blas, "but you have got
the cucumber by the wrong end. We say that January
is in summer."

"Not in my country, where the seasons are reversed,"

106

I said. "When I rose next morning it was dark as night, for a black fog had fallen upon the city."

"A black fog!" exclaimed Lechuza.

"Yes, a black fog that would last all day and make it darker than night, for though the lamps were lighted in the streets they gave no light."

"Demons!" exclaimed Rivarola; "there is no water in the bucket. I must go to the well for some or we shall have none to drink in the night."

"You might wait till I finish," I said.

"No, no, Captain," he returned. "Go on with your story; we must not be without water." And taking up the bucket he trudged off.

"Finding it was going to be dark all day," I continued, "I determined to go a little distance away, not out of London, you will understand, but about three leagues from my hotel to a great hill, where I thought the fog would not be so dark, and where there is a palace of glass."

"A palace of glass!" repeated Lechuza, with his immense round eyes fixed sternly on me.

"Yes, a palace of glass—is there anything so wonderful in that?"

"Have you any tobacco in your pouch, Mariano?" said Blas. "Pardon, Captain, for speaking, but the things you are telling require a cigarette, and my pouch is empty."

"Very well, sirs, perhaps you will now allow me to proceed," I said, beginning to feel rather vexed at these constant interruptions. "A palace of glass large enough to hold all the people in this country."

"The Saints assist us! Your tobacco is dry as ashes, Mariano," exclaimed Blas.

"That is not strange," said the other, "for I have had it three days in my pocket. Proceed, Captain. A palace of glass large enough to hold all the people in the world. And then?"

"No, I shall not proceed," I returned, losing my temper. "It is plain to see that you do not wish to hear my story. Still, sirs, from motives of courtesy you might have disguised your want of interest in what I was about to relate; for I have heard it said that the Orientals are a polite people."

"There you are saying too much, my friend," broke in Lechuza. "Remember that we were speaking of actual experiences, not inventing tales of black fogs and glass palaces and men walking on their heads, and I know not what other marvels."

"Do you know that what I am telling you is untrue?" I indignantly asked.

"Surely, friend, you do not consider us such simple persons in the Banda Oriental as not to know truth from fable?"

W. H. HUDSON—*The Purple Land.*

THE RUNAGATES

Everything was still. It was sundown, and not the faintest breeze stirred the warm, sleepy air.

Along the straggling street, the light lay soft on white-washed houses, rounding the angles, and tingeing the walls, roofs, doorways with a faint, lustrous pink. In the open space of the Chapel of Ease, or at the doors of shops and houses were figures—lolling, or gossiping drowsily in the soft, Devonshire drawl.

In front of the Inn sprawled a spaniel pup all head and legs, playing with its own ears, and gaping helplessly at the children who ran out of by-streets, chased each other lazily, and disappeared. An old man in fustian, with a bushy projecting beard, leaned heavily on a stick against the wall, turning to mutter sleepily to someone within. There was a faint, distant cawing of rooks, a smell of bacon and old hay, of burning wood, of honey-suckle.

Then on the nodding village came the sound of van-wheels, and with it a kind of stir and rustle. That sound of wheels grew louder, then ceased; opposite the Chapel of Ease stood a gipsy van, cavernous, black, weather-stained, with baskets, strings of onions, pans, a tiny blue thread of rising smoke, a smell of old clothes.

The horse stood where it was pulled up, without move-ment, drooping its tired head; by its side a gipsy girl stretched herself, resting on one leg, with her hands at the back of her head, where the light played tricks with her blue-black hair, giving it the colour of bronze.

Lithe as a snake, she glanced from side to side with dark eyes, hitching at her skirt, and settling a dingy scarf across her chest. Her angular features had the oblique cat-like cast of her race.

A broad old man with iron-grey hair and coppery visage leaned over the shaft, and talked to someone inside.

The stir and rustle began again.

Children were running out of houses, shops, alleys, everywhere—boys and girls. In white frocks, coloured frocks, with clean faces, and dirty faces; hustling each other on, then standing quite still.

Their hands were clasped in each other's, their mouths wide open. They stood in a half-ring, many-coloured, hushed, a yard or two from the van, shuffling up the dust with their feet, whispering. Sometimes they would break a little, as if for flight, then close up nearer. An old woman, with thick hair and hooked nose, emerged from the van with a baby in her arms. A little girl clutching at her dress hid behind her. Continual quivers of sound like the trembling of telegraph wires ran through the ring of children.

The old woman put the baby into the man's arms, lifted the child to the front of the van, and moved away, talking quickly to the girl in a low voice. Their figures disappeared amongst the houses, and the ring of children sagged nearer to the van; fingers began to creep out, and point; on the outskirts boys took little runs to and fro.

Slowly the pink flush died out of the light, forms took harder outlines; a faint humming of gnats began; and suddenly the sound of voices broke forth, high-pitched in argument.

The old fellow against the Inn wall spat over the bush of his beard, stretched, called in an angry mutter, and stumped away, leaning on his stick; the spaniel puppy retreated uneasily into the Inn, uttering shrill barks over its shoulder; people came out of doorways, stared at the van, and turning on their heels abruptly vanished.

That foreign thing which had come into the village, had brought with it changes as subtle as the play of light.

The old gipsy stood with his arms leaning on the shaft, whistling and filling a pipe; over against him on the edge of the driving board, sat the child and the baby, flaxen-haired mites with sunburnt faces; both were silent as dolls, and had something doll-like in their looks, as if set out for inspection.

So the ring of children seemed to think, nudging one another and whispering; one or two of the elder girls stretched out their hands to the baby, and drew them back with frightened giggles.

The boys began to play—familiarity had bred contempt in them already; but the girls stood fascinated, their yellow heads bobbing and twisting, their fingers beckoning or pointing.

The light was softening again, becoming greyer, mysterious; things lost certainty in the gloom, receded and wavered; the fitful glimmer of a window lamp grew steady.

The old gipsy's voice began, clear and persuasive, talking to the children. Up the street a concertina had started "Rule, Britannia" in polka time; there were sounds of scuffling and dancing; two voices were raised in the courtyard of the Inn.

A cart came rattling out between the dim houses. A dog barked; the voices of the boys at play grew shriller; there broke out the wailing of a baby, and the skirl of a concertina rising and falling. A woman came out scolding, and dragged two of the girls away:

"What d'yu want with gipsies then? Yu pair of fules."

A group of men surged in a doorway, voluble, laughing; their faces mere blurs, and the bowls of their pipes glowing and sending forth a splutter of sparks. Across the bluish darkness the house-lamps threw out their fan-shaped gleams. In one of them the heads of the old gipsy and the two children were outlined ruddy and gold-coloured against the grim cavern of the van.

Then, as if starting from the earth, the forms of the two women reappeared; the old gipsy withdrew his arms from the shaft, there was a confused mutter, a rapid stir, a girl's uneasy laugh; the old horse gave a jerk forward —the van moved. In front, dragging at the horse's bridle, the bent figure of the gipsy girl slipped, dark and noiseless, into the night; with a heavy rumbling the black van disappeared.

There was a sound like a sigh in the street, a patter of footsteps. A man yawned slowly, another called:

"Yu mind that ther', wull'ee?"

A pipe was knocked out against wood with a sharp tap.

"Waal, mebbe yu're raight. 'Tis main 'ot zurely— gude avenin'.'"

"Gude naight, Wellium."

"Gude naight."

"Yu'le tak' the ole 'arse then?"

"That's as mebbe—waal, gude naight."

"Gude naight."

The sound of voices and receding footsteps yielded to a hush, soft and deep as the blackness of the harvest night. The scent of the freshening earth filled all the drowsy air; a faint breeze like the passing of a spirit went shivering through the village.

Λ dim form stood noiseless in the street, listening to the concertina drawling out the last notes of "Home, Sweet Home." One by one the fan-shaped splashes flickered off the walls; blackness took their place.

JOHN GALSWORTHY—*The Inn of Tranquillity.*

THE DISTRESSES OF A COMMON SOLDIER

No observation is more common, and at the same time more true, than that one half of the world are ignorant how the other half lives. The misfortunes of the great are held up to engage our attention; are enlarged upon in tones of declamation; and the world is called upon to gaze at the noble sufferers: the great, under the pressure of calamity, are conscious of several others sympathizing with their distress; and have, at once, the comfort of admiration and pity.

There is nothing magnanimous in bearing misfortunes with fortitude, when the whole world is looking on: men in such circumstances will act bravely even from motives of vanity; but he who, in the vale of obscurity, can brave adversity; who, without friends to encourage, acquaintances to pity, or even without hope to alleviate his misfortunes, can behave with tranquillity and indifference, is truly great: whether peasant or courtier, he deserves admiration, and should be held up for our imitation and respect.

While the slightest inconveniences of the great are magnified into calamities; while tragedy mouths out their sufferings in all the strains of eloquence, the miseries of the poor are entirely disregarded; and yet some of the lower ranks of people undergo more real hardships in one day, than those of a more exalted station suffer in their whole lives. It is inconceivable what difficulties the meanest of our common sailors and soldiers endure without murmuring or regret; without passionately declaiming against Providence, or calling their fellows to be gazers on their intrepidity. Every day is to them a day of misery, and yet they entertain their hard fate without repining.

With what indignation do I hear an Ovid, a Cicero, or a Rabutin, complain of their misfortunes and hardships, whose greatest calamity was that of being unable to visit a certain spot of earth, to which they had foolishly attached an idea of happiness. Their distresses were pleasures, compared to what many of the adventuring poor every day endure without murmuring. They ate, drank, and slept; they had slaves to attend them, and were sure of subsistence for life: while many of their fellow creatures are obliged to wander without a friend to comfort or assist them, and even without shelter from the severity of the season.

I have been led into these reflections from accidentally meeting, some days ago, a poor fellow, whom I knew when a boy, dressed in a sailor's jacket, and begging at one of the outlets of the town, with a wooden leg. I knew him to have been honest and industrious when in the country, and was curious to learn what had reduced him to his present situation. Wherefore, after giving him what I thought proper, I desired to know the history of his life and misfortunes, and the manner in which he was reduced to his present distress. The disabled soldier, for such he was, though dressed in a sailor's habit, scratching his head, and leaning on his crutch, put himself into an attitude to comply with my request, and gave me his history as follows:

"As for my misfortunes, master, I can't pretend to

have gone through any more than other folks; for, except the loss of my limb, and my being obliged to beg, I don't know any reason, thank Heaven, that I have to complain; there is Bill Tibbs, of our regiment, he has lost both his legs, and an eye to boot; but, thank Heaven, it is not so bad with me yet.

"I was born in Shropshire; my father was a labourer, and died when I was five years old; so I was put upon the parish. As he had been a wandering sort of man, the parishioners were not able to tell to what parish I belonged, or where I was born, so they sent me to another parish, and that parish sent me to a third. I thought in my heart, they kept sending me about so long, that they would not let me be born in any parish at all; but, at last, however, they fixed me. I had some disposition to be a scholar, and was resolved, at least to know my letters; but the master of the workhouse put me to business as soon as I was able to handle a mallet; and here I lived an easy kind of a life for five years. I only worked ten hours in the day, and had my meat and drink provided for my labour. It is true, I was not suffered to stir out of the house, for fear, as they said, I should run away; but what of that, I had the liberty of the whole house, and the yard before the door, and that was enough for me. I was then bound out to a farmer, where I was up both early and late; but I ate and drank well, and liked my business well enough, till he died, when I was obliged to provide for myself; so I was resolved to go seek my fortune.

"In this manner I went from town to town, worked when I could get employment, and starved when I could get none; when happening one day to go through a field belonging to a justice of peace, I spied a hare crossing the path just before me; and I believe the devil put it in my head to fling my stick at it.—Well, what will you have on't? I killed the hare, and was bringing it away, when the justice himself met me: he called me a poacher and a villain; and collaring me, desired I would give an account of myself: I fell upon my knees, begged his worship's pardon, and began to give a full account of all that I knew of my breed, seed, and generation; but though I gave a very true account, the justice said I could give no account; so I was indicted at sessions, found guilty of being poor, and sent up to London to Newgate, in order to be transported as a vagabond.

"People may say this and that of being in jail; but, for my part, I found Newgate as agreeable a place as ever I was in all my life. I had enough to eat and drink, and did no work at all. This kind of life was too good to last for ever; so I was taken out of prison, after five months, put on board a ship, and sent off, with two hundred more, to the plantations. We had but an indifferent passage, for, being all confined in the hold, more than a hundred of our people died for want of sweet air; and those that remained were sickly enough, God knows. When we came ashore, we were sold to the planters—and I was bound for seven years more. As I was no scholar, for I did not know my letters, I was obliged to work among the negroes; and I served out my time, as in duty bound to do.

"When my time was expired, I worked my passage home, and glad I was to see Old England again, because I loved my country. I was afraid, however, that I should be indicted for a vagabond once more, so did not much care to go down into the country, but kept about the town, and did little jobs when I could get them.

"I was very happy in this manner for some time, till one evening, coming home from work, two men knocked me down, and then desired me to stand. They belonged to a press-gang: I was carried before the justice, and, as I could give no account of myself, I had my choice left, whether to go on board a man-of-war, or list for a soldier. I chose the latter; and, in this post of a gentleman, I served two campaigns in Flanders, was at the battles of Val and Fontenoy, and received but one wound, through the breast here; but the doctor of our regiment soon made me well again.

"When the peace came on I was discharged; and as I could not work, because my wound was sometimes troublesome, I listed for a landman in the East India Company's service. I here fought the French in six pitched battles; and I verily believe, that if I could read or write, our captain would have made me a corporal. But it was not my good fortune to have any promotion, for I soon fell sick, and so got leave to return home again with forty pounds in my pocket. This was at the beginning of the present war, and I hoped to be set on shore, and to have the pleasure of spending my money; but the Government wanted men, and so I was pressed for a sailor before ever I could set foot on shore.

"The boatswain found me, as he said, an obstinate fellow: he swore he knew that I understood my business well, but that I shammed Abraham, to be idle; but God knows, I knew nothing of sea-business, and he beat me without considering what he was about. I had still, however, my forty pounds, and that was some comfort

to me under every beating; and the money I might have
had to this day, but that our ship was taken by the
French, and so I lost all.

"Our crew was carried into Brest, and many of them
died, because they were not used to live in jail; but, for
my part, it was nothing to me, for I was seasoned. One
night, as I was sleeping on the bed of boards, with a
warm blanket about me, for I always loved to lie well,
I was awakened by the boatswain, who had a dark
lantern in his hand; 'Jack,' says he to me, 'will you
knock out the French sentries' brains?' 'I don't care,'
says I, striving to keep myself awake, 'if I lend a hand.'
'Then follow me,' says he, 'and I hope we shall do
business.' So up I got, and tied my blanket, which was
all the clothes I had, about my middle, and went with
him to fight the Frenchmen. I hate the French because
they are all slaves, and wear wooden shoes.

"Though we had no arms, one Englishman is able
to beat five French at any time; so we went down to the
door, where both the sentries were posted, and rushing
upon them, seized their arms in a moment, and knocked
them down. From thence, nine of us ran together to
the quay, and seizing the first boat we met, got out of
the harbour and put to sea. We had not been here
three days before we were taken up by the *Dorset*
privateer, who were glad of so many good hands; and we
consented to run our chance. However, we had not as
much luck as we expected. In three days we fell in with
the *Pompadour* privateer, of forty guns, while we had
but twenty-three; so to it we went, yard-arm and yard-
arm. The fight lasted for three hours, and I verily
believe we should have taken the Frenchman, had we
but had some more men left behind; but, unfortunately,

we lost all our men just as we were going to get the victory.

"I was once more in the power of the French, and I believe it would have gone hard with me, had I been brought back to Brest; but, by good fortune, we were retaken by the *Viper*. I had almost forgot to tell you, that, in that engagement, I was wounded in two places: I lost four fingers of the left hand, and my leg was shot off. If I had had the good fortune to have lost my leg and use of my hand on board a king's ship, and not aboard a privateer, I should have been entitled to clothing and maintenance during the rest of my life; but that was not my chance: one man is born with a silver spoon in his mouth, and another with a wooden ladle. However, blessed be God, I enjoy good health, and will for ever love liberty and Old England. Liberty, property, and Old England, for ever, huzza!"

Thus saying, he limped off, leaving me in admiration at his intrepidity and content; nor could I avoid acknowledging, that an habitual acquaintance with misery serves better than philosophy to teach us to despise it.

GOLDSMITH—*Essays*.

THE INN AT EVENING

FEELING now my feet more broken than ever, I very slowly and in sharp shoots of pain dragged down the slope towards the main road: I saw just below me the frontier stones of the Prussians, and immediately within them a hut. To this I addressed myself.

It was an inn. The door opened of itself, and I found there a pleasant woman of middle age, but frowning. She had three daughters, all of great strength, and she was upbraiding them loudly in the German of Alsace and making them scour and scrub. On the wall above her head was a great placard which I read very tactfully, and in a distant manner, until she had restored the discipline of her family. This great placard was framed in the three colours which once brought a little hope to the oppressed, and at the head of it in broad black letters were the three words, " Freedom, Brotherhood, and an Equal Law." Underneath these was the emblematic figure of a cock, which I took to be the Gallic bird, and underneath him again was printed in enormous italics:

> " *Quand ce coq chantera*
> *Ici crédit l'on fera.*"

Which means:

> " When you hear him crowing
> Then's the time for owing.
> Till that day—
> Pay."

While I was still wondering at this epitome of the French people, and was attempting to combine the French military tradition with the French temper in the affairs of economics; while I was also delighting in the memory of the solid coin that I carried in a little leathern bag in my pocket, the hard-working, God-fearing, and honest woman that governs the little house and the three great daughters, within a yard of the frontier, and on the top of this huge hill, had brought back all her troops into line and had the time to attend to me. This she did with the utmost politeness, though cold by race, and through her politeness ran a sense of what Teutons called Duty, which would once have repelled me; but I have wandered over a great part of the world, and I know it now to be a distorted kind of virtue.

She was of a very different sort from that good tribe of the Moselle valley beyond the hill; yet she also was Catholic—(she had a little tree set up before her door for the Corpus Christi: see what religion is, that makes people of utterly different races understand each other; for when I saw that tree I knew precisely where I stood. So once all we Europeans understood each other, but now we are divided by the worst malignancies of nations and classes, and a man does not so much love his own nation as hate his neighbours, and even the twilight of chivalry is mixed up with a detestable patronage of the poor. But as I was saying——) she also was a Catholic, and I knew myself to be with friends. She was moreover not exactly of—what shall I say? the words Celtic and Latin mean nothing—not of those who delight in a delicate manner; and her good heart prompted her to say, very loudly:

" What do you want? "

"I want a bed," I said, and I pulled out a silver coin.
"I must lie down at once."

Then I added, "Can you make omelettes?"

Now it is a curious thing, and one I will not dwell
on—

LECTOR. You do nothing but dwell.

AUCTOR. It is the essence of lonely travel; and if you
have come to this book for literature you have come to
the wrong booth and counter. As I was saying: it is
a curious thing that some people (or races) jump from
one subject to another naturally, as some animals (I
mean the noble deer) go by bounds. While there are
other races (or individuals—heaven forgive me, I am no
ethnologist) who think you a criminal or a lunatic unless
you carefully plod along from step to step like a hippo-
potamus out of water. When, therefore, I asked this
family-drilling, house-managing, mountain-living woman
whether she could make omelettes, she shook her head
at me slowly, keeping her eyes fixed on mine, and said
in what was the corpse of French with a German ghost
in it, "The bed is a franc."

"Motherkin," I answered, "what I mean is that I
would sleep until I wake, for I have come a prodigious
distance and have last slept in the woods. But when I
wake I shall need food, for which," I added, pulling out
yet another coin, "I will pay whatever your charge may
be; for a more delightful house I have rarely met with.
I know most people do not sleep before sunset, but I am
particularly tired and broken."

She showed me my bed then much more kindly, and
when I woke, which was long after dusk, she gave me
in the living-room of the hut eggs beaten up with ham,
and I ate brown bread and said grace.

Then (my wine was not yet finished, but it is an abominable thing to drink your own wine in another person's house) I asked whether I could have something to drink.

"What you like," she said.

"What have you?" said I.

"Beer," said she.

"Anything else?" said I.

"No," said she.

"Why, then, give me some of that excellent beer."

I drank this with delight, paid all my bill (which was that of a labourer), and said good night to them.

In good nights they had a ceremony; for they all rose together and curtsied. Upon my soul I believe such people to be the salt of the earth. I bowed with real contrition, for at several moments I had believed myself better than they. Then I went to my bed and they to theirs. The wind howled outside; my boots were stiff like wood and I could hardly take them off; my feet were so martyrized that I doubted if I could walk at all on the morrow. Nevertheless I was so wrapped round with the repose of this family's virtues that I fell asleep at once. Next day the sun was rising in angry glory over the very distant hills of Germany, his new light running between the pinnacles of the clouds as the commands of a conqueror might come trumpeted down the defiles of mountains, when I fearlessly forced my boots on to my feet and left their doors.

The morning outside came living and sharp after the gale—almost chilly. Under a scattered but clearing sky I first limped, then, as my blood warmed, strode down the path that led between the trees of the farther vale and was soon following a stream that leaped from one fall to another till it should lead me to the main road, to Belfort, to the Jura, to the Swiss whom I had never known, and at last to Italy.

HILAIRE BELLOC—*The Path to Rome.*

A BULLY PUNISHED

I LIVED on very good terms, not only with the master and the old ostler, but with all the domestics and hangers on at the inn; waiters, chambermaids, cooks, and scullions, not forgetting the "boots," of which there were three. As for the postillions, I was sworn brother with them all, and some of them went so far as to swear that I was the best fellow in the world; for which high opinion entertained by them of me, I believe I was principally indebted to the good account their comrade gave of me, whom I had so hospitably received in the dingle. I repeat that I lived on good terms with all the people connected with the inn, and was noticed and spoken kindly to by some of the guests—especially by that class termed commercial travellers—all of whom were great friends and patronizers of the landlord, and were the principal promoters of the dinner, and subscribers to the gift of plate, which I have already spoken of,[1] the whole fraternity striking me as the jolliest set of fellows imaginable, the best customers to an inn, and the most liberal to servants; there was one description of persons, however, frequenting the inn, which I did not like at all, and which I did not get on well with, and these people were the stage-coachmen.

The stage-coachmen of England, at the time of which I am speaking, considered themselves mighty fine gentry,

[1] It was worth at least fifty guineas.

nay, I verily believe the most important personages of the realm, and their entertaining this high opinion of themselves can scarcely be wondered at; they were low fellows, but masters at driving; driving was in fashion, and sprigs of nobility used to dress as coachmen and imitate the slang and behaviour of the coachmen, from whom occasionally they would take lessons in driving as they sat beside them on the box, which post of honour any sprig of nobility who happened to take a place on a coach claimed as his unquestionable right; and these sprigs would smoke cigars and drink sherry with the coachmen in bar-rooms, and on the road; and, when bidding them farewell, would give them a guinea or a half-guinea, and shake them by the hand, so that these fellows, being low fellows, very naturally thought no small liquor of themselves, but would talk familiarly of their friends lords so-and-so, the honourable misters so-and-so, and Sir Harry and Sir Charles, and be wonderfully saucy to anyone who was not a lord, or something of the kind; and this high opinion of themselves received daily augmentation from the servile homage paid them by the generality of the untitled male passengers, especially those on the fore part of the coach, who used to contend for the honour of sitting on the box with the coachman when no sprig was nigh to put in his claim. Oh! what servile homage these craven creatures did pay these same coach fellows, more especially after witnessing this or t'other act of brutality practised upon the weak and unoffending—upon some poor friendless woman travelling with but little money, and perhaps a brace of hungry children with her, or upon some thin and half-starved man travelling on the hind part of the coach from London to Liverpool with only eighteen pence in his pocket after his fare was paid, to defray his expenses on the road; for as the insolence of these knights was vast, so was their rapacity enormous; they had been so long accustomed to have crowns and half-crowns rained upon them by their admirers and flatterers, that they would look at a shilling, for which many an honest labourer was happy to toil for ten hours under a broiling sun, with the utmost contempt; would blow upon it derisively, or fillip it into the air before they pocketed it; but when nothing was given them, as would occasionally happen—for how could they receive from those who had nothing? and nobody was bound to give them anything, as they had certain wages from their employers—then what a scene would ensue! Truly the brutality and rapacious insolence of English coachmen had reached a climax; it was time that these fellows should be disenchanted, and the time—thank Heaven! —was not far distant. Let the craven dastards who used to curry favour with them, and applaud their brutality, lament their loss now that they and their vehicles have disappeared from the roads; I, who have ever been an enemy to insolence, cruelty, and tyranny, loathe their memory, and, what is more, am not afraid to say so well aware of the storm of vituperation, partly learnt from them, which I may expect from those who used to fall down and worship them.

Amongst the coachmen who frequented the inn was one who was called "the bang-up coachman." He drove to our inn, in the fore part of every day, one of what were called the fast coaches, and afterwards took back the corresponding vehicle. He stayed at our house about twenty minutes, during which time the passengers of the coach which he was to return with dined; those at least who were inclined for dinner, and could pay for it. He derived his sobriquet of "the bang-up coachman" partly from his being dressed in the extremity of coach dandyism, and partly from the peculiar insolence of his manner, and the unmerciful fashion in which he was in the habit of lashing on the poor horses committed to his charge. He was a large tall fellow, of about thirty, with a face which, had it not been bloated by excess, and insolence and cruelty stamped most visibly upon it, might have been called good-looking. His insolence indeed was so great, that he was hated by all the minor fry connected with coaches along the road upon which he drove, especially the ostlers, whom he was continually abusing or finding fault with. Many was the hearty curse which he received when his back was turned; but the generality of people were much afraid of him, for he was a swinging strong fellow, and had the reputation of being a fighter, and in one or two instances had beaten in a barbarous manner individuals who had quarrelled with him.

I was nearly having a fracas with this worthy. One day, after he had been drinking sherry with a sprig, he swaggered into the yard where I happened to be standing; just then a waiter came by carrying upon a tray part of a splendid Cheshire cheese, with a knife, plate, and napkin. Stopping the waiter, the coachman cut with the knife a tolerably large lump out of the very middle of the cheese, stuck it on the end of the knife, and putting it to his mouth nibbled a slight piece off it, and then, tossing the rest away with disdain, flung the knife down upon the tray, motioning the waiter to proceed; "I wish," said I, "you may not want before you die what you have just flung away," whereupon the fellow turned furiously towards me; just then, however, his coach being standing at the door, there was a cry for coachman, so that he was forced to depart, contenting himself for the present with shaking his fist at me, and threatening to serve me out on the first opportunity; before, however, the opportunity occurred he himself got served out in a most unexpected manner.

The day after this incident he drove his coach to the inn, and after having dismounted and received the contributions of the generality of the passengers, he strutted up, with a cigar in his mouth, to an individual who had come with him, and who had just asked me a question with respect to the direction of a village about three miles off, to which he was going. "Remember the coachman," said the knight of the box to this individual, who was a thin person of about sixty, with a white hat, rather shabby black coat, and buff-coloured trousers, and who held an umbrella and a small bundle in his hand. "If you expect me to give you anything," said he to the coachman, "you are mistaken; I will give you nothing. You have been very insolent to me as I rode behind you on the coach, and have encouraged two or three trumpery fellows, who rode along with you, to cut scurvy jokes at my expense, and now you come to me for money; I am not so poor, but I could have given you a shilling had you been civil; as it is, I will give you nothing." "Oh! you won't, won't you?" said the coachman; "dear me! I hope I shan't starve because you won't give me anything—a shilling! why, I could afford to give you twenty if I thought fit, you pauper! civil to you, indeed! things are come to a fine pass if I need be civil to you! Do you know who you are speaking to? why, the best lords in the country are proud to speak to me. Why, it was only the other day that the Marquis of —— said to me——" and then he went on to say what the Marquis said to him; after which, flinging down his cigar, he strutted up the road, swearing to himself about paupers.

"You say it is three miles to ——," said the individual to me; "I think I shall light my pipe, and smoke it as I go along." Thereupon he took out from a side-pocket a tobacco-box and short meerschaum pipe, and implements for striking a light, filled his pipe, lighted it, and commenced smoking. Presently the coachman drew near. I saw at once that there was mischief in his eye; the man smoking was standing with his back towards him, and he came so nigh to him, seemingly purposely, that as he passed a puff of smoke came of necessity against his face. "What do you mean by smoking in my face?" said he, striking the pipe of the elderly individual out of his mouth. The other, without manifesting much surprise, said, "I thank you; and if you will wait a minute, I will give you a receipt for that favour"; then gathering up his pipe, and taking off his coat and hat, he laid them on a stepping-block which stood near, and rubbing his hands together, he advanced towards the coachman in an attitude of offence, holding his hands crossed very near to his face. The coachman, who probably expected anything but such a movement from a person of the age and appearance of the individual whom he had insulted, stood for a moment motionless with surprise; but, recollecting himself, he pointed at him derisively with his finger; the next moment, however, the other was close upon him, had struck aside the extended hand with his left fist, and given him a severe blow on the nose with his right, which he immediately followed by a left-hand blow in the eye; then drawing his body slightly backward, with the velocity of lightning he struck the coachman full in the mouth, and the last blow was the severest of all, for it cut the coachman's lips nearly through; blows so quickly and sharply dealt I had never seen. The coachman reeled like a fir-tree in a gale, and seemed nearly unsensed. "Ho! what's this? a fight! a fight!" sounded from a dozen voices, and people came running from all directions to see what was going on. The coachman, coming somewhat to himself, disencumbered himself of his coat and hat; and, encouraged by two or three of his brothers of the whip, showed some symptoms of fighting, endeavouring to close with his foe, but the attempt was vain, for his foe was not to be closed with; he did not shift or dodge about, but warded off the blows of his opponent with the greatest sang-froid, always using the guard which I have already described, and putting in, in return, short chopping blows with the swiftness of lightning. In a very few minutes the countenance of the coachman was literally cut to pieces, and several of his teeth were dislodged; at length he gave in; stung with mortification, however, he repented, and asked for another round; it was granted, to his own complete demolition. The coachman did not drive his coach back that day, he did not appear on the box again for a week; but he never held up his head afterwards. Before I quitted the inn, he had disappeared from the road, going no one knew where.

GEORGE BORROW—*The Romany Rye.*

IMPRESSIONS OF HOLLAND

ROTTERDAM,
3 *Aug.*, 1716.

I FLATTER myself, dear sister, that I shall give you some
pleasure in letting you know that I have safely passed
the sea, though we had the ill fortune of a storm. We
were persuaded by the captain of the yacht to set out in
a calm, and he pretended there was nothing so easy as
to tide it over; but after two days' slowly moving, the
wind blew so hard that none of the sailors could keep
their feet, and we were all Sunday night tossed very
handsomely. I never saw a man more frighted than
the captain.

For my part, I have been so lucky as neither to suffer
from fear nor seasickness; though I confess I was so
impatient to see myself once more upon dry land that I
would not stay till the yacht could get to Rotterdam,
but went in the long boat to Helvoetsluys, where we had
voitures to carry us to the Briel.

I was charmed with the neatness of that little town;
but my arrival at Rotterdam presented me a new scene
of pleasure. All the streets are paved with broad stones,
and before many of the meanest artificers' doors are
placed seats of various-coloured marbles, so neatly kept
that I'll assure you I walked almost all over the town
yesterday, incognito, in my slippers, without receiving
one spot of dirt; and you may see the Dutch maids
washing the pavement of the street with more applica-

tion than ours do our bedchambers. The town seems so full of people, with such busy faces all in motion, that I can hardly fancy it is not some celebrated fair; but I see it is every day the same. It is certain no town can be more advantageously situated for commerce. Here are seven large canals, on which the merchants' ships come up to the very doors of their houses. The shops and warehouses are of a surprising neatness and magnificence, filled with an incredible quantity of fine merchandise, and so much cheaper than what we see in England that I have much ado to persuade myself I am still so near it. Here is neither dirt nor beggary to be seen. One is not shocked with those loathsome cripples so common in London, nor teased with the importunity of idle fellows and wenches, that choose to be nasty and lazy. The common servants and little shopwomen here are more nicely clean than most of our ladies, and the great variety of neat dresses—every woman dressing her head after her own fashion—is an additional pleasure in seeing the town.

You see hitherto I make no complaints, dear sister, and if I continue to like travelling as well as I do at present, I shall not repent my project. It will go a great way in making me satisfied with it if it affords me an opportunity of entertaining you. But it is not from Holland that you must expect a disinterested offer. I can write enough in the style of Rotterdam to tell you plainly in one word that I expect returns of all the London news. You see I have already learnt to make a good bargain, and that it is not for nothing I will so much as tell you I am

Your affectionate sister.

LADY MARY WORTLEY MONTAGU—*Letters.*

GEYSERS

The rest of our day's journey lay through a country less interesting than the district we had traversed before luncheon. For the most part we kept on along the foot of the hills, stopping now and then for a drink of milk at the occasional farms perched upon their slopes. Sometimes turning up a green and even bushy glen (there are no trees in Iceland, the nearest approach to anything of the kind being a low dwarf birch, hardly worthy of being called a shrub), we would cut across the shoulder of some projecting spur, and obtain a wider prospect of the level land upon our right; or else keeping more down in the flat, we had to flounder for half an hour up to the horses' shoulders in an Irish bog. After about five hours of this work we reached the banks of a broad and rather singular river, called the Brúará. Half-way across it was perfectly fordable; but exactly in the middle was a deep cleft, into which the waters from either side spilt themselves, and then in a collected volume roared over a precipice a little lower down. Across this cleft some wooden planks were thrown, giving the traveller an opportunity of boasting that he had crossed a river on a bridge which itself was under water. By this time we had all begun to be very tired, and very hungry—it was 11 o'clock p.m. We had been twelve or thirteen hours on horseback, not to mention

occasional half-hours of pretty severe walking after the
ptarmigan and plover. Many were the questions we
addressed to Sigurdr on the distance yet remaining, and
many the conjectures we hazarded as to whether the
cook would have arrived in time to get dinner ready for
us. At last, after another two hours' weary jogging, we
descried, straight in front, a low steep brown rugged hill,
standing entirely detached from the range at the foot
of which we had been riding; and in a few minutes more,
wheeling round its outer end, we found ourselves in the
presence of the steaming Geysers.

I do not know that I can give you a better notion of
the appearance of the place than by saying that it looked
as if—for about a quarter of a mile—the ground had
been honeycombed by disease into numerous sores and
orifices; not a blade of grass grew on its hot, inflamed
surface, which consisted of unwholesome-looking red
livid clay, or crumpled shreds and shards of slough-like
incrustations. Naturally enough, our first impulse on
dismounting was to scamper off at once to the Great
Geyser. As it lay at the farthest end of the congeries of
hot springs, in order to reach it we had to run the gaunt-
let of all the pools of boiling water and scalding quag-
mires of soft clay that intervened, and consequently
arrived on the spot with our ankles nicely poulticed.
But the occasion justified our eagerness. A smooth
siliceous basin, seventy-two feet in diameter and four
feet deep, with a hole at the bottom as in a washing-
basin on board a steamer, stood before us brimful of
water just upon the simmer; while up into the air above
our heads rose a great column of vapour, looking as if it
was going to turn into the Fisherman's Genie. The
ground about the brim was composed of layers of in-

crusted silica, like the outside of an oyster, sloping gently down on all sides from the edge of the basin.

Having satisfied our curiosity with this cursory inspection of what we had come so far to see, hunger compelled us to look about with great anxiety for the cook; and you may fancy our delight at seeing that functionary in the very act of dishing up dinner on a neighbouring hillock. Sent forward at an early hour, under the chaperonage of a guide, he had arrived about two hours before us, and seizing with a general's eye the key of the position, at once turned an idle babbling little Geyser into a camp-kettle, dug a bake-house in the hot soft clay, and improvising a kitchen-range at a neighbouring vent, had made himself completely master of the situation. It was about one o'clock in the morning when we sat down to dinner, and as light as day.

As the baggage-train with our tents and beds had not yet arrived, we fully appreciated our luck in being treated to so dry a night; and having eaten everything we could lay hands on, were sat quietly down to chess, and coffee brewed in Geyser water; when suddenly it seemed as if beneath our very feet a quantity of subterraneous cannon were going off; the whole earth shook, and Sigurdr, starting to his feet, upset the chess-board (I was just beginning to get the best of the game), and flung off full speed towards the great basin. By the time we reached its brim, however, the noise had ceased, and all we could see was a slight movement in the centre, as if an angel had passed by and troubled the water. Irritated at this false alarm, we determined to revenge ourselves by going and tormenting the Strokr. Strokr —or *the churn*—you must know, is an unfortunate Geyser, with so little command over his temper and his stomach, that you can get a *rise* out of him whenever you like. All that is necessary is to collect a quantity of sods, and throw them down his funnel. As he has no basin to protect him from these liberties, you can approach to the very edge of the pipe, about five feet in diameter, and look down at the boiling water which is perpetually seething at the bottom. In a few minutes the dose of turf you have just administered begins to disagree with him; he works himself up into an awful passion—tormented by the qualms of incipient sickness, he groans and hisses, and boils up, and spits at you with malicious vehemence, until at last, with a roar of mingled pain and rage, he throws up into the air a column of water forty feet high, which carries with it all the sods that have been chucked in, and scatters them scalded and half-digested at your feet. So irritated has the poor thing's stomach become by the discipline it has undergone, that even long after all foreign matter has been thrown off, it goes on retching and sputtering, until at last nature is exhausted, when, sobbing and sighing to itself, it sinks back into the bottom of its den.

Put into the highest spirits by the success of his performance, we turned away to examine the remaining springs. I do not know, however, that any of the rest are worthy of particular mention. They all resemble in character the two I have described, the only difference being that they are infinitely smaller, and of much less power and importance. One other remarkable formation in the neighbourhood must not be passed unnoticed. Imagine a large irregular opening in the surface of the soft white clay, filled to the very brim with scalding water, perfectly still, and of as bright a blue as that of the Grotto Azzuro at Capri, through whose transparent depths you can see down into the mouth of a vast sub-aqueous cavern, which runs, Heaven knows how far, in a horizontal direction beneath your feet. Its walls and varied cavities really looked as if they were built of the purest lapis lazuli—and so thin seemed the crust that roofed it in, we almost fancied it might break through and tumble us all into the fearful beautiful bath.

Having by this time taken a pretty good look at the principal features of our new domain, I wrapped myself up in a cloak and went to sleep; leaving orders that I should not be called until after the tent had arrived, and our beds were ready. Sigurdr followed my example, but the Doctor went out shooting.

As our principal object in coming so far was to see an eruption of the Great Geyser, it was of course necessary we should wait his pleasure; in fact, our movements entirely depended upon his. For the next two or three days, therefore, like pilgrims round some ancient shrine, we patiently kept watch; but he scarcely deigned to vouchsafe us the slightest manifestation of his latent energies. Two or three times the cannonading we had heard immediately after our arrival recommenced—and once an eruption to the height of about ten feet occurred; but so brief was its duration, that by the time we were on the spot, although the tent was not eighty yards distant, all was over. As after every effort of the fountain the water in the basin mysteriously ebbs back into the funnel, this performance, though unsatisfactory in itself, gave us an opportunity of approaching the mouth of the pipe and looking down into its scalded gullet. In an hour afterwards the basin was brimful as ever.

LORD DUFFERIN—*Letters from High Latitudes.*

PORTUGAL IN 1796

TO JOSEPH COTTLE

LISBON,
1 *February*, 1796.

THE city is a curious place; a straggling plan; built on the most uneven ground, with heaps of ruins in the middle and large open places. The streets filthy beyond all English ideas of filth; for they throw everything into the streets, and nothing is removed. Dead animals annoy you at every corner; and such is the indolence and nastiness of the Portuguese, that I verily believe they would let each other rot, in the same manner, if the priests did not get something by burying them. Some of the friars are avowed to wear their clothes without changing for a year; and this is a comfort to them: you will not wonder, therefore, that I always keep to the windward of these reverend perfumers.

The streets are very agreeable in wet weather. If you walk under the houses, you are drenched by the water-spouts. If you attempt the middle, there is a river. If you would go between both, there is the dunghill. The rains here are very violent, and the streams in the streets on a declivity, so rapid as to throw down men; and sometimes to overset carriages. A woman was drowned some years ago in one of the most frequented streets of Lisbon.

To-night I shall see the procession of " Our Lord of the Passion." This image is a very celebrated one, and with great reason, for one night he knocked at the door of St. Roque's church, and there they would not admit him. After this he walked to the other end of the town, to the church of St. Grace, and there they took him in; but a dispute now arose between the two churches, to which the image belonged; whether to the church which he first chose, or the church that first chose him. The matter was compromised. One church has him, and the other fetches him for their processions, and he sleeps with the latter the night preceding. The better mode for deciding it had been to take the gentleman between both, and let him walk to which he liked best. What think you of this story being believed in 1796!!!

The power of the Inquisition still exists, though they never exercise it, and thus the Jews save their bacon. Fifty years ago it was the greatest delight of the Portuguese to see a Jew burnt. Geddes, the then chaplain, was present at one of these detestable Autos da Fé. He says, " The transports expressed by all ages, and all sexes, whilst the miserable sufferers were shrieking and begging mercy for God's sake, formed a scene more horrible than any out of hell! " He adds, that " this barbarity is not their national character, for no people sympathize so much at the execution of a criminal."

It is as warm here as in May with you; of course we broil in that month at Lisbon; but I shall escape the hot weather here, as I did the cold weather of England, and quit this place the latter end of April. You will, of course, see me the third day after my landing at Falmouth, or, if I can get companions in a postchaise sooner. This my resolution is like the law of the Medes and Persians, that altereth not. Be so good as to procure for me a set of Coleridge's *Watchman*, with his lectures and Poems. I want to write a Tragedy here, but can find no leisure to begin with.

Portugal is much plagued with robbers, and they generally strip a man, and leave him to walk home in his birthday suit. An Englishman was served thus at Almeyda, and the Lisbon magistrates, on his complaint, took up the whole village, and imprisoned them all. Contemplate this people in what light you will, you can never see them in a good one. They suffered their best epic Poet to perish for want; and they burnt to death their best dramatic writer, because he was a Jew.

Yours,
ROBERT SOUTHEY.

ROBERT SOUTHEY—*Letters.*

LAPLAND

WE were all on our legs at daybreak, the whole camp
was astir to see me off.   I distributed among my friends
my much appreciated little presents of tobacco and
sweets, and they all wished me God-speed.   If all went
well I was to arrive the next day at Forsstugan, the
nearest human habitation in the wilderness of marshes,
torrents, lakes and forests which was the home of the
homeless Lapps.   Ristin, Turi's sixteen-year-old grand-
daughter, was to be my guide.   She knew a few words
of Swedish, she had been once before to Forsstugan, she
was to push on from there to the nearest church village
to join the Lapp school once more.

Ristin walked in front of me in her long white reindeer tunic and red woollen cap.   Round her waist she
wore a broad leather belt, embroidered with blue and
yellow thread and studded with buckles and squares of
solid silver.   Suspended from her belt hung her knife,
her tobacco pouch and her mug.   I also noticed a small
axe for cutting wood stuck under the belt.   She wore
leggings of soft, white reindeer-skin, fastened to her wide
skin-breeches. Her small feet were stuck in dainty, white
reindeer shoes neatly trimmed with blue thread.   On
her back she carried her *laukos*, a knapsack of birch-bark
containing her various belongings and our provisions.
It was twice as big as my own rucksack, but she did not

seem to mind it in the least. She moved down on the steep slope with the rapid, noiseless step of an animal, jumped, swift as a rabbit, over a fallen tree-trunk or a pool of water. Now and then she sprang, agile as a goat, on to a steep rock, looking round in all directions. At the foot of the hill we came upon a broad stream, I had hardly time to wonder how we were to get across before she was in the water up to her hips, there was nothing for me to do but to follow her in the ice-cold water. I soon got warm again as we ascended the steep opposite slope at an amazing speed. She hardly ever spoke and it mattered little, for I had the greatest difficulty to understand what she said. Her Swedish was as bad as my Laplandish. We sat down on the soft moss to an excellent meal of rye biscuits, fresh butter and cheese, smoked reindeer's tongue and delicious cool water from the mountain brook in Ristin's mug. We lit our pipes and tried again to understand each other's speech.

" Do you know the name of that bird? " said I.

" Lahol," smiled Ristin, recognizing at once the soft, flute-like whistle of the dotterel, who shares their solitude with the Lapps and is much beloved by them.

From a willow-bush came the wonderful song of the bluethroat.

" Jilow! Jilow! " laughed Ristin.

The Lapps say that the bluethroat has a bell in his throat and that he can sing one hundred different songs. High over our heads hung a black cross riveted to the blue sky. It was the royal eagle, surveying on motionless wings his desolate kingdom. From the mountain lake came the weird call of the loon.

" Ro, ro, raik," repeated Ristin faithfully. She said

it meant: " fine weather to-day, fine weather to-day! "
When the loon said: " Var luk, var luk, luk, luk," it
meant: " it is going to rain again, it is going to rain
again, again," Ristin informed me.

I lay there stretched out full length on the soft moss,
smoking my pipe and watching Ristin carefully arrang-
ing her belongings in her laukos.   A small blue woollen
shawl, an extra pair of neat, little reindeer shoes, a pair
of beautiful embroidered red gloves to wear in church,
a Bible.   Again I was struck with the refined shape of
her small hands, common to all Lapps.   I asked her
what was in the little box cut out of a birch-root?   As
I could not understand a word of her long explanation
in her mixed tongue of Swedish, Finnish and Laplandish
I sat up and opened the box.   It contained what looked
like a handful of earth.   What was she going to do
with it?

Again she tried her best to explain, again I failed to
understand her.   She shook her head impatiently, I
am sure she thought I was very stupid.   Suddenly she
stretched herself full length on the moss and lay quite
still and stiff with closed eyes.   Then she sat up and
scratched the moss for a handful of earth which she
handed me with a very serious face.   Now I understood
what was in the birch-root box.   It contained a little
earth from the grave in the wilderness where a Lapp
had been buried last winter under the snow.   Ristin was
to take it to the priest who was to read the Lord's Prayer
over it and sprinkle it over the churchyard.

We shouldered our knapsacks and set off again.   As
we descended the slope, the aspect of the landscape
changed more and more.   We wandered over immense
tundras covered with carex grass and here and there

patches of bright yellow clusters of cloud-berries which we picked and ate as we passed along. The solitary Dwarf-birches, the *betula nana* of the heights, grew into groves of silver birches, intermixed with aspen and ash and thickets of willow-elder, bird-cherry and wild currant. Soon we entered a dense forest of stately fir-trees. A couple of hours later we were walking through a deep gorge walled in by steep, moss-covered rocks. The sky over our heads was still bright with evening sun but it was already almost dark in the ravine. Ristin glanced uneasily around her, it was evident that she was in a hurry to get out of the gorge before night-fall. Suddenly she stood still. I heard the crashing of a broken tree-branch and I saw something dark looming in front of me at a distance of less than fifty yards.

"Run," whispered Ristin, white in the face, her little hand grasping the axe in her belt.

I was quite willing to run had I been able to do so. As it was, I stood still, riveted to the spot by a violent cramp in the calf of my legs. I could now see him quite well. He was standing knee-deep in a thicket of bilberries, a twig full of his favourite berries was sticking out of his big mouth, we had evidently interrupted him in the midst of his supper. He was of uncommonly large size, by the shabby look of his coat evidently a very old bear, no doubt the same bear Turi had told me about.

"Run," I whispered in my turn to Ristin with the gallant intention of behaving like a man and covering her retreat. The moral value of this intention was however diminished by the fact that I was still completely unable to move. Ristin did not run. Instead of running away she made me witness an unforgettable

scene, enough to repay a journey from Paris to Lapland.
You are quite welcome to disbelieve what I am going to
tell you, it matters little to me. Ristin, one hand on her
axe, advanced a few steps towards the bear. With her
other hand raising her tunic, she pointed out the wide
leather breeches which are worn by the Lapp women.
The bear dropped his bilberry twig, sniffed loudly a
couple of times and shuffled off among the thick firs.

"He likes bilberries better than me," said Ristin as
we set off again as fast as we could.

Ristin told me that when her mother had brought
her back from the Lapp school in the spring, they had
come upon the old bear almost at the same place in
the midst of the gorge and that he had scrambled
away as soon as her mother had shown him she was a
woman.

Soon we emerged from the gorge and wandered
through the darkening forest on a carpet of silvery grey
moss, soft as velvet and interwoven with bunches of
Linnaea and Pyrola. It was neither light nor dark, it
was the wonderful twilight of the northern summer
night. How Ristin could find her way through the
trackless forest was incomprehensible to my stupid
brain. All of a sudden we came upon our friend the
brook again. I had just time to bend down to kiss his
night-cool face as he rushed past us. Ristin announced
it was time for supper. With incredible rapidity she
chopped some wood with her axe and lit the camp fire
between two boulders. We ate our supper, smoked our
pipes and were soon fast asleep, our rucksacks under our
heads. I was awakened by Ristin presenting me her
red cap full of bilberries; no wonder the old bear liked
bilberries, I never had a better breakfast. On we went.

Hallo! there was our friend the brook again joyously
dancing along over hillocks and stones and singing in
our ears that we had better come along with him down
to the mountain lake. So we did lest he should lose his
way in the gloom. Now and then we lost sight of him
but we heard him singing to himself the whole time.
Now and then he stopped to wait for us by a steep rock
or a fallen tree to rush away again faster than ever to
make up for lost time. A moment later there was no
longer any fear he might lose his way in the gloom for
the night had already fled on swift goblin feet deeper
into the forest. A flame of golden light quivered in the
tree-tops.

"Piavi!" said Ristin, "the sun is rising!"

Through the mist of the valley at our feet a mountain
lake opened its eyelid.

I approached the lake with uneasy forebodings of
another ice-cold bath. Luckily I was mistaken. Ristin
stopped short before a small *eka*, a flat-bottomed boat,
half-hidden under a fallen fir-tree. It belonged to
nobody and to everybody, it was used by the Lapps on
their rare visits to the nearest church village to exchange
their reindeer-skins for coffee, sugar and tobacco, the
three luxuries of their lives. The water of the lake was
cobalt blue, even more beautiful than the sapphire blue
of the Blue Grotto in Capri. It was so transparent that
I thought I almost could see the hole the terrible Stalo
had knocked in its bottom. Half across the lake we
met two stately travellers swimming side by side, their
superb antlers high out of the water. Luckily they
mistook me for a Lapp so we could come up so close to
them that I could see their soft beautiful eyes looking

fearlessly at us.   There is something very strange about the eyes of the elk as about those of the reindeer, they always seem to be looking straight at your own eyes at whatever angle you see them.   We climbed rapidly the steep opposite shore and wandered once more over an immense marshy plain with nothing to guide us but the sun.   My attempts to explain to Ristin the use of my pocket compass had met with so little success that I had given up looking at it myself, putting my trust in Ristin's instinct of a half-tame animal.   It was evident that she was in a great hurry, ere long I had the impression that she was not sure of our way.   Now and then she set off as fast as she could in one direction, stopped short to sniff the wind with quivering nostrils, then she darted off in another direction to repeat the same manœuvre. Now and then she bent down to smell the ground like a dog.

" *Rog*," she said suddenly pointing to a low cloud moving towards us with extraordinary rapidity across the marshes.

Fog indeed!   In a minute we were enveloped in a thick mist as impenetrable as a November fog in London.   We had to hold each other by the hand not to lose sight of one another.   We struggled on for another hour or two, knee deep in the ice-cold water. At last Ristin said she had lost our direction, we must wait till the fog was over.   How long might it last?

She did not know, perhaps a day and a night, perhaps an hour, it all depended upon the wind.   It was one of the worst experiences I have ever gone through.   I knew quite well that with our scanty equipment the encounter with a fog on the immense swamps was far more dangerous than the encounter with a bear in the forest. I also knew that there was nothing to do but to wait where we were. We sat for hours on our knapsacks, the fog sticking to our skin as a sheet of ice cold water. My misery was complete when I was going to light my pipe and found my waistcoat pocket full of water. While I was still staring dejectedly at my soaked match-box, Ristin had already struck fire with her tinder-box and lit her pipe. Another defeat for civilization was when I wanted to put on a pair of dry socks and discovered that my waterproof knapsack of best London make was soaked through and through and that all Ristin's belongings in her home-made laukos of birch-bark were dry as hay. We were just waiting for the water to boil for a well-needed cup of coffee when a sudden gush of wind blew out the flame of my little spirit lamp. Ristin was off in an instant in the direction of the wind and back again to order me to put on my rucksack at once. In less than a minute a strong steady wind was blowing straight in our faces and the curtain of mist lifted rapidly over our heads. Deep below in the valley at our very feet we saw a huge river glistening in the sun like a sword. Along the opposite shore stretched out a dark pine forest as far as the eye could see. Ristin lifted her hand and pointed to a thin column of smoke rising over the tree-tops.

"Forsstugan," said Ristin.

She sprang down the slope and without a moment's hesitation she plunged into the river up to her shoulders and I after her. Soon we lost our footing and swam across the river as the elks had swum across the forest lake. After half an hour's walk through the forest on the other side of the river we reached a clearing evidently made by the hand of man.   A huge Lapland dog came rushing towards us full-speed barking fiercely.   After much sniffing at us he was overjoyed to see us and proceeded to lead the way with a friendly wagging of his tail.

AXEL MUNTHE—*The Story of San Michele.*

A PARTY IN THE DESERT

MEANWHILE the local families promised unlimited hospitality, and Nasir, Lawrence, Nesib, Zeki and the rest were bound to accept it. Every morning they had to go to a different guest-tent and eat an enormous meal. About fifty men were present at each of these feasts and the food was always served on the same enormous copper dish, five feet across, which was lent from host to host and belonged really to Auda. It was always the same boiled mutton and rice, two or three whole sheep making a pyramid of meat in the middle with an embankment of rice all round, a foot wide and six inches deep, filled with legs and ribs of mutton. In the very centre were the boiled sheeps' heads propped upright with flapping ears and jaws pulled open to show the teeth. Cauldrons of boiling fat, full of bits of liver, intestines, skin, odd scraps of meat, were poured over the great dish until it began to overflow on the ground; and at this sign the host called them all to eat. They would rise with good-mannered shyness and crowd about the bowl, twenty-two at a time, each man kneeling on one knee.

Taking their time from Nasir, the most honourable man of the company, they rolled up their right sleeves, said grace and dipped together with their fingers. Only the right hand might be used, for good manners. Lawrence always dipped cautiously; his fingers could hardly

bear the hot fat. Nobody was allowed to talk, for it
was an insult to the host not to appear to be very hungry
indeed, eating at top speed. The host himself stood by
and encouraged their appetites as they dipped, tore and
gobbled. At last eating gradually slackened and each
man crouched with his elbow on his knee, the hand
hanging down from the wrist to drip over the edge of
the tray. When all had finished Nasir cleared his throat
for a signal and they rose together in haste, muttering,
"God requite it to you, host," and then made room for
the next twenty-two men. The more dainty eaters
wiped the grease off their hands on a flap of the roof-
cloth intended for this purpose. Then sighingly all sat
down on carpets, while slaves splashed water over their
hands and the tribal cake of soap went round. When
the last man had eaten and coffee had been served, the
guests remounted with a quiet blessing. Instantly the
children would rush for what was left, and tear the
gnawed bones from one another; some would escape
with valuable pieces, to eat them safely behind a distant
bush, the dogs yapping about finishing what was left.
Nesib and Zeki soon broke down under this continual
feeding, not being used to desert hospitality, so Nasir
and Lawrence had to go out twice a day for a week and
eat for the honour of Feisal.

On May the thirtieth they went forward again in
company with the whole of the Abu Tayi; it was the
first time that Lawrence had ever taken part in the
march routine of a Bedouin tribe. There was no appar-
ent order, but the caravan advanced simultaneously on
a wide front, each family making a self-contained party.
The men were on riding-camels; the black goat-hair
tents and the howdahs in which the women were hidden

were carried on the baggage-camels. Farraj and Daud
were behaving with more than usual mischief in this
care-free atmosphere. They rode about leaving a trail
of practical jokes behind them. Particularly they made
jokes about snakes. Sirhan was visited that summer
by a plague of snakes—horned vipers, puff-adders, cobras
and black snakes. By night movement was dangerous
and at last the party learned to beat the bushes with
sticks as they walked. It was dangerous to draw water
after dark, for snakes swam in the pools or gathered in
clusters on their brinks. Twice puff-adders invaded the
coffee-hearth, twisting among the seated men.

Lawrence's party of fifty killed about twenty snakes
daily. Seven men were bitten. Three died, four
recovered after great fear and pain. The Howeitat treatment was to bind up the bite with snake-skin plaster and
read chapters of the Koran to the patient until he died.
They also pulled on thick blue-tasselled red ankle-boots
from Damascus over their feet when they went out at
night. The snakes loved warmth and at night would lie
beside the sleepers under or on the blankets: so great
care was taken in getting up each morning. The constant danger was getting on everyone's nerves except
Farraj's and Daud's. They thought it very witty to
raise false alarms and give furious beatings to harmless
twigs and roots: at last Lawrence at a noonday halt
forbade them ever again to call out "Snakes!" About
an hour later, sitting on the sand, he noticed them
smiling and nudging one another. His glance idly
followed theirs to a bush close by where lay coiled a
brown snake, about to strike at him.

He threw himself to one side and called out to another
of his men, who jumped at the snake with a riding-cane

and killed it. Lawrence then told him to give the boys half a dozen strokes with the cane to teach them not to take things too literally at his expense. Nasir, dozing beside Lawrence, woke up shouting: "And six more from me!" Nesib and Zeki and the rest who had all suffered from the boys' bad sense of humour called out for more punishment still. However, Lawrence saved Farraj and Daud from the full weight of their companions' anger; instead he proclaimed them moral outcasts and set them to gather sticks and draw water under the charge of the women, the greatest disgrace for sixteen-year-olds who counted themselves men.

The tribe moved on from well to well—the water always brackish—through a landscape of barren palms and bushes which were no use for grazing or firewood and only served to harbour snakes. At last they reached a place called Ageila where they came on a village of tents, and out rode Auda to meet them. He had a strong escort with him of Ruwalla horsemen, which showed that he had had success with Nuri. The Ruwalla, bareheaded and yelling, with brandished spears and wild firing of rifles and revolvers, welcomed the party to Nuri's empty house.

Here they stopped, pitched their tents, and received deputations from the clans and gifts of ostrich eggs, Damascus dainties, camels and scraggy horses. Three men were set to make coffee for the visitors, who came in to Nasir as Feisal's deputy and took the oath of allegiance to the Arab movement, promising to obey Nasir and follow him. Their presents included an unintentional one of lice; so that long before sunset Nasir and Lawrence were nearly mad with irritation. Auda had a stiff left arm due to an old wound, but experience had taught him how to poke a camel-stick up his left sleeve and turn it round and round against his ribs, which relieved the itch a good deal.

Nebk was the place decided upon for a rallying ground, it had plentiful water and some grazing. Here Nasir and Auda sat down for days to discuss together how to enrol the volunteers and prepare the road to Akaba, now about a hundred and eighty miles to the west. This left Nesib, Zeki and Lawrence at leisure. As usual the Syrians let their imagination run ahead of them. In their enthusiasm they forgot all about Akaba and their immediate purpose, and spoke of marching straight to Damascus, rousing the Druse and Shaalan Arabs on the way. The Turks would be taken by surprise and the final objective won without troubling about the steps between.

ROBERT GRAVES—*Lawrence and the Arabs.*

THE GREAT FIRE

September 2, 1666.   This fatal night, about ten, began the deplorable fire, near Fish Street, in London.

September 3.   The fire continuing, after dinner, I took coach with my wife and son, and went to the Bankside in Southwark, where we beheld that dismal spectacle, the whole city in dreadful flames near the water-side; all the houses from the Bridge, all Thames Street, and upwards towards Cheapside, down to the Three Cranes, were now consumed; and so returned, exceedingly astonished what would become of the rest.

The fire having continued all this night (if I may call that night which was light as day for ten miles round about, after a dreadful manner), when conspiring with a fierce eastern wind in a very dry season, I went on foot to the same place; and saw the whole south part of the city burning from Cheapside to the Thames, and all along Cornhill (for it likewise kindled back against the wind as well as forward), Tower Street, Fenchurch Street, Gracechurch Street, and so along to Baynard's Castle, and was now taking hold of St. Paul's Church, to which the scaffolds contributed exceedingly.

The conflagration was so universal, and the people so astonished that, from the beginning, I know not by what despondency or fate, they hardly stirred to quench it; so that there was nothing heard or seen but crying out and lamentation, running about like distracted creatures, without at all attempting to save even their goods, such a strange consternation there was upon them, so as it burned both in breadth and length, the churches, public halls, Exchange, hospitals, monuments and ornaments, leaping after a prodigious manner from house to house, and street to street, at great distances one from the other. For the heat, with a long set of fair and warm weather, had even ignited the air, and prepared the materials to conceive the fire which devoured, after an incredible manner, houses, furniture, and everything.

Here we saw the Thames covered with goods floating, all the barges and boats laden with what some had time and courage to save, as, on the other side the carts, etc., were carrying out to the fields, which for many miles were strewed with movables of all sorts, and tents erected to shelter both people and what goods they could get away. All the sky was of a fiery aspect, like the top of a burning oven, and the light seen above forty miles roundabout for many nights. God grant mine eyes may never behold the like. The noise and crackling and thunder of the impetuous flames, the shrieking of women and children, the hurry of people, the fall of towers, houses, and churches, was like a hideous storm, and the air all about so hot and inflamed that at the last one was not able to approach it, so that they were forced to stand still, and let the flames burn on. The clouds of smoke were dismal, and reached near fifty miles in length.

September 4. The burning still rages, and it is now gotten as far as the Inner Temple. All Fleet Street, the Old Bailey, Ludgate Hill, Warwick Lane, Newgate,

Paul's Chain, Watling Street are now flaming, and most of it reduced to ashes. The stones of Paul's flew like grenados,[1] the melting lead running down the streets in a stream, and the very pavements glowing with fiery redness, so as no horse nor man was able to tread on them. The eastern wind still more impetuously driving the flames forward.

September 5. It crossed towards Whitehall; but oh, the confusion there was then at Court. It pleased His Majesty to command me, among the rest, to look after the quenching of Fetter Lane end, to preserve (if possible) that part of Holborn; whilst the rest of the gentlemen took their several posts, some at one part, and some at another, for now they began to bestir themselves, and to consider that nothing was likely to put a stop but the blowing up of so many houses as might make a wider gap than any had yet been made. It was therefore now commanded, and my concern being particularly for the Hospital of St. Bartholomew, near Smithfield, where I had many wounded and sick men,[2] made me the more diligent to promote it.

It now pleased God, by abating the wind, and by the industry of the people, infusing a new spirit into them, that the fury of it began sensibly to abate about noon, so as it came no farther than the Temple westward, nor than the entrance of Smithfield north: but continued all this day and night so impetuous towards Cripplegate and the Tower as made us all despair.

The poor inhabitants were dispersed about St. George's Fields, and Moorfields, as far as Highgate, and several miles in circle, some under tents, some under miserable

---

[1] Hand grenades.
[2] Casualties in the Dutch War.

huts and hovels, many without a rag or any necessary utensils, bed or board.

September 6. *Thursday.* It is not indeed imaginable how extraordinary the vigilance and activity of the King and Duke was, even labouring in person and being present to command, order, reward or encourage workmen, by which he showed his affection to his people, and gained theirs.

September 7. I went this morning on foot from Whitehall as far as London Bridge, through the late Fleet Street, Ludgate Hill by St. Paul's, Cheapside, Exchange, Bishopsgate, Aldersgate and out to Moorfields, thence through Cornhill, etc., with extraordinary difficulty, clambering over heaps of yet smoking rubbish, and frequently mistaking where I was; the ground under my feet as hot that it even burnt the soles of my shoes.

In the meantime, His Majesty got to the Tower by water, to demolish the houses about the graff,[1] which, being built entirely about it, had they taken fire and attacked the White Tower, where the magazine of powder lay, would undoubtedly not only have beaten down and destroyed all the Bridge, but sunk and torn the vessels in the river, and rendered the demolition beyond all expression for several miles about the country.

At my return I was infinitely concerned to find that goodly Church, St. Paul's—now a sad ruin, and that beautiful portico (not long before repaired by the late King) now rent in pieces, flakes of large stones split asunder, and nothing remaining entire but the inscription in the architrave showing by whom it was built,

---

[1] Moat.

which had not one letter of it defaced. It was astonishing to see what immense stones the heat had in a manner calcined, so that all the ornaments, columns, friezes, capitals, and projectures of massy Portland stone, flew off, even to the very roof, where a sheet of lead covering a great space (no less than six acres by measure) was totally melted. The ruins of the vaulted roof falling, broke into St. Faith's, which being filled with the magazines of books belonging to the Stationers, and carried hither for safety, they were all consumed, burning for a week following.

The exquisitely wrought Mercers' Chapel, the sumptuous Exchange, the august fabric of Christ Church, all the rest of the Companies' Halls, splendid buildings—all in dust; the fountains dried up and ruined, whilst the very waters remained boiling; cellars, wells, and dungeons, formerly warehouses, still burning in stench and dark clouds of smoke, so that in five or six miles traversing about I did not see one load of timber consumed, nor many stones but what were calcined white as snow.

The people, who now walked about the ruins, appeared like men in some dismal desert, or rather, in some great city laid waste by a cruel enemy. Sir Thomas Gresham's statue, though fallen from its niche in the Royal Exchange, remained entire, when all those of the Kings since the Conquest were broken to pieces, while the vast iron chains of the City streets, hinges, bars, and gates of prisons were many of them melted and reduced to cinders by the vehement heat. Nor was I yet able to pass through any of the narrow streets, but kept the widest; the ground and air, smoke and fiery vapour continued so intense that my hair was almost singed, and my feet unsufferably surbated.[1]   The bye-lanes and narrow streets were quite filled up with rubbish, nor could one have possibly known where he was but by the ruins of some Church or Hall that had some remarkable tower or pinnacle remaining.

[1] Sore.

EVELYN—*Diary.*

A DAY IN THE COUNTRY

14th. (Lord's day.) Up, and my wife, a little before four, and to make us ready; and by and by Mrs. Turner came to us by agreement, and she and I stayed talking below while my wife dressed herself, which vexed me that she was so long about it, keeping us till past five o'clock before she was ready. She ready; and taking some bottles of wine, and beer, and some cold fowl with us into the coach, we took coach and four horses, which I had provided last night, and so away. A very fine day, and so towards Epsom, talking all the way pleasantly, and particularly of the pride and ignorance of Mrs. Lowther, in having of her train carried up. The country very fine, only the way very dusty. To Epsom, by eight o'clock, to the well; where much company, and I drank the water: they did not, but I did drink four pints. And to the town, to the King's Head. W. Hewer rode with us, and I left him and the women, and myself walked to the church, where few people to what I expected, and none I knew, but all the Houblons, brothers, and them after sermon I did salute, and walk with towards my inn. . . .

We parted to meet anon, and I to my women into a better room, which the people of the house borrowed for us, and there to a good dinner, and were merry, and Pembleton came to us, who happened to be in the house, and there talked and were merry.

163

After dinner, he gone, we all lay down (the day being wonderful hot) to sleep, and each of us took a good nap, and then rose; and here Tom Wilson came to see me, and sat and talked an hour; and I perceive he hath been much acquainted with Dr. Fuller (Tom) and Dr. Pierson, and several of the great cavalier parsons during the late troubles; and I was glad to hear him talk of them, which he did very ingenuously, and very much of Dr. Fuller's art of memory, which he did tell me several instances of.

By and by he parted, and we took coach and to take the air, there being a fine breeze abroad; and I carried them to the well, and there filled some bottles of water to carry home with me; and there I talked with the two women that farm the well, at £12 per annum, of the lord of the manor. . . .

Here W. Hewer's horse broke loose, and we had the sport to see him taken again. Then I carried them to see my cousin Pepys's house, and 'light, and walked round about it, and they like it, as indeed it deserves, very well, and is a pretty place; and then I walked them to the wood hard by, and there got them in the thickets till they lost themselves, and I could not find the way into any of the walks in the wood, which indeed are very pleasant, if I could have found them.

At last got out of the wood again; and I, by leaping down the little bank, coming out of the wood, did sprain my right foot, which brought me great pain, but presently, with walking, it went away for the present, and so the women and W. Hewer and I walked upon the Downes, where a flock of sheep was; and the most pleasant and innocent sight that ever I saw in my life. We found a shepherd and his little boy reading, far from any houses or sight of people, the Bible to him; so I made the boy read to me, which he did, with the forced tone that children do usually read, that was mighty pretty, and then I did give him something, and went to the father, and talked with him; and I find he had been a servant in my cousin Pepys's house, and told me what was become of their old servants. He did content himself mightily in my liking his boy's reading, and did bless God for him, the most like one of the old patriarchs that ever I saw in my life, and it brought those thoughts of the old age of the world in my mind for two or three days after.

We took notice of his woollen knit stockings of two colours mixed, and of his shoes shod with iron, both at the toe and heels, and with great nails in the soles of his feet, which was mighty pretty; and, taking notice of them, " why," says the poor man, " the Downs, you see, are full of stones, and we are fain to shoe ourselves thus; and these," says he, " will make the stones fly till they ring before me." I did give the poor man something, for which he was mighty thankful, and I tried to cast stones with his horn crook. He values his dog mightily, that would turn a sheep any way which he would have him, when he goes to fold them: told me there was about eighteen score sheep in his flock, and that he hath four shillings a-week the year round for keeping of them: and Mrs. Turner, in the common fields here, did gather one of the prettiest nosegays that ever I saw in my life.

So to our coach, and through Mrs. Minnes's wood, and looked upon Mr. Evelyn's house; and so over the common, and through Epsom town to our inn, in the way stopping a poor woman with her milk-pail, and in one of my gilt tumblers did drink our bellyfuls of milk, better than any cream; and so to our inn, and there had a dish of cream, but it was sour, and so had no pleasure in it; and so paid our reckoning, and took coach, it being about seven at night, and passed and saw the people walking with their wives and children to take the air, and we set out for home, the sun by and by going down, and we in the cool of the evening all the way with much pleasure home, talking and pleasing ourselves with the pleasure of this day's work. Mrs. Turner mightily pleased with my resolution, which, I tell her, is never to keep a country-house, but to keep a coach, and with my wife on the Saturday to go sometimes for a day to this place, and then quit to another place; and there is more variety and as little charge, and no trouble, as there is in a country-house.

Anon it grew dark, and we had the pleasure to see several glowworms, which was mighty pretty, but my foot begins more and more to pain me so that when we came home, which was just at eleven at night, I was not able to walk from the lane's end to my house without being helped. So to bed, and there had a cere-cloth[1] laid to my foot, but in great pain all night long.

[1] Plaster.

PEPYS—*Diary*.

MY CORONATION

Thursday, 28 June, 1838.

I was awoke at four o'clock by the guns in the Park, and could not get much sleep afterwards on account of the noise of the people. Got up at seven, feeling strong and well; the Park presented a curious spectacle, crowds of people up to Constitution Hill, soldiers, bands, &c. I dressed, having taken a little breakfast before I dressed, and a little after. At half-past 9 I went into the next room, dressed exactly in my House of Lords costume.

At 10 I got into the State Coach with the Duchess of Sutherland and Lord Albemarle and we began our Progress. It was a fine day and the crowds of people exceeded what I have ever seen; many as there were the day I went to the City, it was nothing, nothing to the multitudes, the millions of my loyal subjects, who were assembled *in every spot* to witness the Procession. Their good humour and excessive loyalty was beyond everything, and I really cannot say *how* proud I feel to be the Queen of *such* a Nation. I was alarmed at times for fear that the people would be crushed and squeezed on account of the tremendous rush and pressure.

I reached the Abbey amid deafening cheers at a little after half-past eleven; I first went into a robing-room quite close to the entrance where I found my eight train-bearers, all dressed alike and beautifully in white satin and silver tissue with wreaths of silver corn-ears in front, and a small one of pink roses round the plait behind, and pink roses in the trimming of the dresses.

After putting on my mantle, and the young ladies having properly got hold of it and Lord Conyngham holding the end of it, I left the robing-room and the Procession began. The sight was splendid; the bank of Peeresses quite beautiful all in their robes, and the Peers on the other side. My young train-bearers were always near me, and helped me whenever I wanted anything. The Bishop of Durham stood on the side near me, but he was, as Lord Melbourne[1] told me, remarkably *maladroit*,[2] and never could tell me what was to take place. At the beginning of the Anthem I retired to St. Edward's Chapel, a dark small place immediately behind the Altar, with my ladies and train-bearers—took off my crimson robe and kirtle; and put on the supertunica of cloth of gold, also in the shape of a kirtle, which was put over a singular sort of little gown of linen trimmed with lace; I also took off my circlet of diamonds and then proceeded bareheaded into the Abbey; I was then seated upon St. Edward's chair, where the Dalmatic robe was clasped round me by the Lord Great Chamberlain. Then followed all the various things; and last of those things the Crown being placed on my head—which was, I must own, a most beautiful impressive moment; *all* the Peers and Peeresses put on their coronets at the same instant.

My excellent Lord Melbourne, who stood very close

[1] Prime Minister.
[2] Clumsy.

to me throughout the whole ceremony, was *completely* overcome at this moment, and very much affected; he gave me *such* a kind, and I may say *fatherly* look. The shouts, which were very great, the drums, the trumpets, the firing of the guns, all at the same instant, rendered the spectacle most imposing.

The Enthronization and the Homage of, first, all the Bishops, and then my Uncles, and lastly of all the Peers, in their respective order was very fine. The Duke of Norfolk (holding for me the Sceptre with a Cross) with Lord Melbourne stood close to me on my right, and the Duke of Richmond with the other Sceptre on my left. All my train-bearers, &c., standing behind the Throne. Poor old Lord Rolle, who is 82, and dreadfully infirm, in attempting to ascend the steps fell and rolled quite down, but was not the least hurt; when he attempted to re-ascend them I got up and advanced to the end of the steps, in order to prevent another fall. When Lord Melbourne's turn to do Homage came, there was loud cheering; they also cheered Lord Grey and the Duke of Wellington; it's a pretty ceremony; they first all touch the Crown, and then kiss my hand. When my good Lord Melbourne knelt down and kissed my hand, he pressed my hand and I grasped his with all my heart, at which he looked up with his eyes filled with tears and seemed much touched, as he was, I observed, throughout the ceremony. After the homage was concluded I left the Throne, took off my Crown and received the Sacrament; I then put on my Crown again, and re-ascended the Throne, leaning on Lord Melbourne's arm. At the commencement of the Anthem I descended from the Throne, and went into St. Edward's Chapel with my Ladies, Train-bearers, and Lord Willoughby, where

I took off the Dalmatic robe, supertunica, &c., and put on the Purple Velvet Kirtle and Mantle, and proceeded again to the Throne, which I ascended leaning on Lord Melbourne's hand.

I then again descended from the Throne, and repaired with all the Peers bearing the Regalia, my Ladies and Train-bearers to St. Edward's Chapel, as it is called; but which, as Lord Melbourne said, was more *un*like a Chapel than anything he had ever seen; for what was *called* an *Altar* was covered with sandwiches, bottles of wine, &c., &c. The Archbishop came in and *ought* to have delivered the Orb to me, but I had already got it, and he (as usual) was *so* confused and puzzled and knew nothing, and—went away. Here we waited some minutes. Lord Melbourne took a glass of wine, for he seemed completely tired. The Procession being formed, I replaced my Crown (which I had taken off for a few minutes), took the Orb in my left hand and the Sceptre in my right, and thus *loaded*, proceeded through the Abbey—which resounded with cheers, to the first robing-room; where I found the Duchess of Gloucester, Mamma, and the Duchess of Cambridge with their Ladies. And here we waited for at least an hour, with *all* my ladies and train-bearers; the Princesses went away about half an hour before I did. The Archbishop had (most awkwardly) put the ring on the wrong finger, and the consequence was that I had the greatest difficulty to take it off again, which I at last did with great pain. Lady Fanny, Lady Wilhelmina, and Lady Mary Grimston looked quite beautiful. At about half-past four I re-entered my carriage, the Crown on my head, and the Sceptre and Orb in my hands, and we proceeded the same way as we came—the crowds if possible having increased.   The enthusiasm, affection, and loyalty were really touching, and I shall ever remember this day as the *Proudest* of my life!   I came home at a little after six, really *not* feeling tired.

Queen Victoria's Journal.

THE DEATH OF CAPTAIN COOK

At the approach of evening on February 13, the commander of the *Discovery's* watering-party came to inform Mr. King that several chiefs were assembled near the beach and were driving away the natives who assisted the sailors in rolling the casks to the shore; at the same time he declared that their behaviour seemed exceedingly suspicious, and that he imagined they would give him some further trouble. Mr. King therefore went himself to the spot, attended by a marine with his musket. At their approach the islanders threw away their stones, and, on Mr. King's application to some of the chiefs, the mob was dispersed. Everything being now quiet, Mr. King went to meet Captain Cook, who was then coming on shore in the pinnace. He related to him what had happened, and received orders to fire a ball at the offenders if they again behaved insolently. In consequence of these directions, Mr. King gave orders to the corporal that the sentinels' pieces should be loaded with ball instead of shot.

On our return to the tents, we heard a continued fire of muskets from the *Discovery* directed at a canoe which was hastening towards the shore with one of our small boats in pursuit of it. This firing, we concluded, was in consequence of some theft, and Captain Cook ordered Mr. King to follow him with a marine armed, and to endeavour to seize the people as they landed. They accordingly ran to the place where the canoe was expected to come ashore, but did not arrive in time, the people having quitted it and fled into the country before their arrival. At this time they did not know that the goods had been already restored, and thinking it probable that they might be of importance, they did not relinquish their endeavours to recover them. Having inquired of the natives what course the people had taken, they pursued them till it was almost dark, when they supposed themselves to be about three miles from the tents, and thinking the islanders amused them with false information in their pursuit, they gave up the search and returned.

A difference of a more serious nature had happened during their absence. The officer who had been dispatched in the small boat after the thieves, and who was returning on board with the booty that had been restored, seeing Captain Cook and Mr. King engaged in pursuit of the offenders, seized a canoe which was drawn up on the shore. This canoe, unfortunately, belonged to Pareea,[1] who, at this instant arriving from the *Discovery*, claimed his property and protested his innocence. The officer persisted in detaining it, in which he was encouraged by the crew of the pinnace then waiting for Captain Cook. A scuffle ensued, and Pareea was knocked down by a violent blow on the head with an oar. Several of the natives, who had hitherto been peaceable spectators, began now to attack our people with such a shower of stones that they were forced to a precipitate retreat, and swam off to a rock at a considerable distance from the shore. The pinnace

[1] A friendly chief.

was plundered immediately by the natives, and would have been entirely demolished if Pareea had not interposed. He had not only recovered from his blow, but had also forgotten it at the same instant. He ordered the crowd to disperse, and beckoned to our people to come and take possession of the pinnace, and afterwards assured them that he would use his influence to get the things which had been taken out of it restored. After their departure he followed them in his canoe, bringing them a midshipman's cap, and some other articles, and expressing much concern at what had happened. He begged to know if the *Orono*[1] would kill him, and whether he might be permitted to come on board the next day. He was assured that he would be well received, and thereupon joined noses with the officers (their usual token of friendship) and paddled over to Kowrowa.

Captain Cook, when these particulars were represented to him, was exceedingly concerned, and when he and Mr. King were returning on board he expressed his fears that these islanders would oblige him to pursue violent measures, adding that they must not be permitted to suppose that they had gained an advantage over us. It was then, however, too late to take any steps that evening; he therefore only gave orders that every islander should be immediately turned out of the ship. This order being executed, Mr. King returned on shore, and the events of the day having much abated our former confidence in the natives, a double guard was posted on the *Morai*, with orders to let Mr. King know if any men were lurking about the beach. At eleven o'clock five of the natives were seen creeping round the

[1] A title given to Captain Cook by the islanders.

bottom of the *Morai*; they approached with great caution, and at last perceiving they were discovered, immediately retired out of sight. About midnight one of them ventured near the observatory, when a sentinel fired over him, on which they all fled, and we had no further disturbance during the remainder of the night. At daylight the next morning Mr. King went on board the *Resolution* in order to get the time-keeper, and on his way thither was hailed by the *Discovery*, who told him that their cutter had been stolen from the buoy where it had been moored during the night.

On Mr. King's return on board, he found the marines were arming themselves, and Captain Cook was loading his double-barrelled gun. Whilst he was acquainting him with what had happened in the night at the *Morai*, he eagerly interrupted him and informed him of the loss of the *Discovery's* cutter, and of the preparations he was making to recover it. It was his usual practice in all the islands of this ocean, when anything of consequence had been stolen from him, to get the king or some of the principal chiefs on board and detain them as hostages till the property was restored. This method having hitherto proved successful, he meant to adopt it on the present occasion, and gave orders to stop every canoe that should attempt to leave the bay, resolving to seize and destroy them if the cutter could not be recovered by peaceable means. In pursuance of which orders, the boats of both ships, properly manned and armed, were stationed across the bay, and before Mr. King quitted the ship some great guns were fired at two canoes that were attempting to escape.

Between seven and eight o'clock Captain Cook and

Mr. King quitted the ship together, the former in the pinnace with Phillips and nine marines, and the latter in the small boat. The last orders Mr. King received from Captain Cook were to quiet the minds of the people on his side of the bay by the strongest assurances that they should not be injured; to keep his people together, and to be continually on his guard. Captain Cook and Mr. King then separated, the captain going towards Kowrowa, where Terreeoboo resided, and Mr. King proceeding to the beach. His first business when he arrived on shore was to issue strict orders to the marines to continue within the tent, to charge their muskets with ball, and not on any consideration to quit their arms. He then attended old Kaoo and the priests at their respective huts, and explained to them, as well as he was able, the reason of the hostile preparations which had so exceedingly alarmed them. He found they were no strangers to the circumstance of the cutter's being stolen, and assured them that though the commodore was not only resolved to recover it, but also to punish in the most exemplary manner the authors of the theft, yet that they and all the inhabitants of the village had not the least occasion to be alarmed, or to apprehend the least danger from us. He importuned the priests to communicate this to the people, and entreat them not to entertain the least idea of fear, but to continue peaceable and quiet. Kaoo asked Mr. King with great emotion if any harm was to happen to Terreeoboo. He assured him there was not, and both he and his brethren appeared satisfied with this assurance.

Captain Cook, having in the meantime called off the launch from the north point of the bay and taken it with him, landed at Kowrowa with the lieutenant and nine marines. He proceeded immediately into the village, where he was respectfully received, the people as usual prostrating themselves before him, and making their accustomed offerings of small hogs. Perceiving that his design was not suspected, his next step was to inquire for the king, and the two boys, his sons, who had been almost continually his guests on board the *Resolution*. The boys presently returned with the natives who had been searching for them, and immediately conducted Captain Cook to the habitation where Terreeoboo had slept. The old man had just awakened, and after some conversation respecting the loss of the cutter, from which the commodore was convinced that he was not in any wise privy to it, he invited him to accompany him and spend the day on board the *Resolution*. The king accepted the invitation, and arose immediately to accompany him.

Everything had now a prosperous appearance; the two boys were already in the pinnace, and the rest of the party were approaching the water-side, when a woman, the mother of the boys, and one of Terreeoboo's favourite wives, followed him, beseeching him, with tears and entreaties, not to venture to go on board. Two chiefs who came with her took hold of him, and insisting he should proceed no farther, obliged him to sit down. The islanders were now collecting in vast numbers along the shore, and having probably been alarmed by the firing of the great guns and the hostile appearances in the bay, gathered round Captain Cook and Terreeoboo. The lieutenant of marines, perceiving that his men were huddled together in the crowd, and consequently unable to use their arms if there should be a necessity for it, proposed to Captain Cook to draw them up along the rocks close to the edge of the water. The populace making way for them to pass, the lieutenant drew them up in a line within about thirty yards of the place where Terreeoboo was sitting.

The old king continued all this time on the ground, bearing the most visible marks of terror and dejection in his countenance. Captain Cook, unwilling to abandon the object which occasioned him to come on shore, urged him most earnestly to proceed; whilst, on the other hand, if the king expressed any inclination to follow him, the chiefs, who surrounded him, interposed; at first they had recourse to prayers and entreaties, but afterwards to force and violence, and even insisted on his remaining on shore. Captain Cook perceiving that there was not a probability of getting him off without much bloodshed, gave up the point; at the same time observing to Mr. Phillips that to compel him to go on board would probably occasion the loss of many lives.

Notwithstanding this enterprise had now failed and was abandoned by Captain Cook, yet it did not appear that his person was in the least degree in danger, till an accident happened which occasioned a fatal turn to the affair. The boats stationed across the bay, having fired at some canoes that attempted to get out, unfortunately killed one of their principal chiefs. Intelligence of his death arrived at the village where Captain Cook then was, just as he had parted from the king and was proceeding with great deliberation towards the shore. The ferment it immediately occasioned was but too conspicuous; the women and children were immediately sent away, and the men were soon clad in their war-mats, and armed with spears and stones. One of the natives, having provided himself with a stone and a long iron spike (called by the natives a *pahooa*), advanced towards the captain, flourishing his weapon in defiance, and threatening to throw the stone. The captain requested him to desist, but the islander repeating his menaces, he was highly provoked, and fired a load of small-shot at him. The man was shielded in his war-mat, which the shot could not penetrate; his firing therefore served only to irritate and encourage them. Volleys of stones were thrown at the marines, and one of the chiefs attempted the life of Mr. Phillips with his *pahooa*; but, not succeeding in the attempt, he received from him a blow with the butt end of his piece. Captain Cook immediately discharged his second barrel, loaded with ball, and killed one of the most violent of the assailants. A general attack with stones succeeded followed on our part by a discharge of musketry, not only from the marines, but also from the people in the boats. The natives, to our great astonishment, received our fire with great firmness, and without giving time to the marines to charge again, they rushed in upon them with dreadful shouts and yells. What followed was a scene of horror and confusion which can be more easily conceived than properly related.

Four of the marines retreated among the rocks, and fell a sacrifice to the fury of the enemy; three others were dangerously wounded, and the lieutenant was stabbed between the shoulders with a *pahooa*; but having fortunately reserved his fire, he shot the man from whom he had received the wound at the instant he was preparing to repeat the blow. The last time our unfortunate commodore was distinctly seen, he was standing at the water's edge and ordering the boats to cease firing and pull in.

It was imagined by some of those who were present that the marines, and those who were in the boats, fired without Captain Cook's orders, and that he was anxious to prevent the further effusion of blood; it is therefore probable that on this occasion his humanity proved fatal to him, for it was observed that while he faced the natives no violence had been offered to him, but when he turned about to give directions to the boats, he was stabbed in the back, and fell with his face into the water. A general shout was set up by the islanders on seeing him fall, and his body was dragged inhumanly on shore. There he was surrounded by the enemy, who, snatching the dagger from each other's hands, displayed a savage eagerness to join in his destruction.

Such was the fate of our most excellent Commander! After a life distinguished by such successful enterprises, his death can hardly be reckoned premature, since he lived to accomplish the great work for which he seemed particularly designed, being rather removed from the enjoyment than the acquisition of glory. How sincerely his loss was lamented by those who owed their security to his skill and conduct, and every consolation to his tenderness and humanity, it is impossible to describe; and the task would be equally difficult to represent the horror, dejection, and dismay which followed so dreadful and unexpected a catastrophe.

The Voyages of Captain Cook.

BIOGRAPHICAL NOTES

BEVIS AT WORK, from *Bevis*, by Richard Jefferies.

Richard Jefferies (1848-1887) was born in a Wiltshire farmhouse. Throughout his book we can feel the breath of the English countryside and a boyish spirit of adventure. He was an ardent naturalist, a great observer of just those details a boy loves to read about. Before we have gone far we are kneeling beside Bevis, now perplexed with his problems, but soon triumphant when his ready resource has discovered how to solve them.

THE SWAN'S NEST, from *Earlham*, by Percy Lubbock.

Percy Lubbock (1879) was educated at Eton and King's College, Cambridge.

Those who consider country life dull and marshlands uninteresting should dip further into this charming book. The author's style is smooth and easy but never monotonous, for there will suddenly flash out a passage of rich colour or of swift action.

Like Jefferies, he has the power to awaken and sustain an interest in apparently trivial things until we soon learn much of the lore of the true nature-lover.

EARLY LIFE, from *The Life of Charles Dickens*, by John Forster.

Charles Dickens (1812-1870) was one of the world's greatest novelists because of his humour and his wide sympathies. Something of the vigour and robustness of his style is due, probably, to the hardships he faced during his boyhood.

Although the London he described has almost vanished, and with it many familiar character types, his popularity has suffered little because of this, for his ready championship of the oppressed awakes a universal response.

Dickens's powerful genius impressed itself deeply on all he wrote. It is a great achievement of his friend, John Forster, that Dickens's personality shines throughout his biography.

THE VILLAGE IDIOT, from *The Natural History of Selborne*, by Gilbert White.

Gilbert White (1720-1793) was an ardent lover of nature. He wished his book to inspire others to write the history of their districts. Thus he was a pioneer of nature-study. His book is full of fascinating detail: he tells of quaint old customs and superstitions of the peasants, and of interesting topics such as whether goats breathe through their ears; nature's providing the deer with additional nostrils; and a wonderful method of curing cancers by means of toads. On nearly every page there is something new to learn: his range of knowledge is astonishingly wide. We learn that owls hoot usually in B flat!

As time advanced Gilbert White became increasingly deaf and missed many of the delights of the countryside.

CHARLES II AFTER WORCESTER, from *King Charles the Second*, by Arthur Bryant.

Arthur Bryant (1899) was educated at Harrow and Queen's College, Oxford. He is a wide reader in historical subjects, and his book contains copious references to original documents.

There are many accounts of the wanderings of Charles after the Battle of Worcester (1651), but none is so vivid in detail or so historically accurate as Mr. Bryant's narrative.

MY ESCAPE FROM THE BOERS, from *My Early Life*, by Winston Churchill.

Winston Churchill (1874) was educated at Harrow and Sandhurst. As Home Secretary, First Lord of the Admiralty, and Chancellor of the Exchequer, he has held important posts in the Cabinet.

My Early Life is written in a style that is light and clear, full of humour and a kindly humanity. It speaks of exciting adventures on the North-West Frontier of India, in the Sudan, and in South Africa. It is interesting to note that Mr. Churchill's captor in the Boer War was later to become the famous General Botha.

WHALING, from *Moby Dick*, by Herman Melville (1819-1891).

Those who have read Frank Bullen's *The Cruise of the Cachalot* will notice a new spirit in *Moby Dick*. Here the whale is regarded as something more than man's natural prey. The White Whale, Moby Dick, " a sperm whale of uncommon magnitude and malignity," is conceived more as a spirit, a manifestation of the colossal forces of nature. Compared with this, man seems but a puny creature. " Oh, man! . . . model thyself after the whale! "

The author is steeped in the lore of the sea: his digressions are always fascinating.

THE CHINA TEA RACE, from *The Bird of Dawning*, by John Masefield.

John Masefield (1878) is the Poet Laureate.

The Bird of Dawning is the most stirring of Mr. Masefield's novels. It is full of the seaman's spirit of courage in the face of grave danger. When the *Blackgauntlet* sinks, sixteen of her crew take to an open boat. They endure almost incredible hardships before sighting a deserted ship, *The Bird of Dawning*. They not only sail this ship home, but are first in the China Tea Race—and win the reward of £200 a head.

BIOGRAPHICAL NOTES

EAST, HALF SOUTH, from *The Brassbounder*, by David W. Bone.

David William Bone (1874) is a Scotsman who entered the Merchant Service in 1890 and served for seven years in sailing vessels before going aboard steamships. He has written several books about sea life, *Broken Stowage*, *Merchantmen-at-Arms*, *The Lookoutman*, and *Capstan Bars*.

The Brassbounder shows the seaman as he really is, and makes no attempt to gloss over the dangers and hardships of his life. The men are all " hard cases," but they are full of a dogged determination to bring their ship safely through her voyage. Their language may be coarsely picturesque, but it is true to life and adds to the vividness of the book.

FOUR JOVIAL SPORTSMEN, from *The Compleat Angler*, by Izaak Walton (1593-1683).

Professor Saintsbury speaks of the " singular golden simplicity " of Walton's style. *The Compleat Angler* is a " haunt of ancient peace," but for all that its characters move actively and with a sprightly grace.

THE ADDER'S STING, from *The Return of the Native*, by Thomas Hardy.

Thomas Hardy (1840-1928) was one of the greatest English novelists. His books have great dramatic power. It is hardly criticism to say that his work is pessimistic; it is fraught with the deeper sense of tragic realism, of the remorselessness of fate. However, the reader cannot fail to notice Hardy's appreciation of human courage.

A trivial incident, a slight misunderstanding, is by a turn of fate magnified into deadly significance. The episode narrated in our extract follows one of these crises.

NOTHING BUT THE TRUTH, from *The Purple Land*, by W. H. Hudson.

William Henry Hudson (1841-1922) was born near Buenos Aires. *The Naturalist in La Plata* is perhaps his most popular book. He was awarded a Civil List Pension of £150 a year as a tribute to "the originality of his writings on natural history." The remembrance of his love for bird life is enshrined in the Bird Sanctuary in Hyde Park.

The Purple Land that England Lost is a romance of Uruguay, revealing the humour, the courtesy, and grace of its people.

THE RUNAGATES, from *The Inn of Tranquillity*, by John Galsworthy.

John Galsworthy (1867-1933) was educated at Harrow and Queen's College, Oxford. He was famous for his plays, *Strife, Loyalties,* and *The Silver Box,* and for his monumental novel, *The Forsyte Saga.*

The Inn of Tranquillity is full of pleasing impressions of country life and sketches of London characters told in crisp dialogue.

THE DISTRESSES OF A COMMON SOLDIER, from Goldsmith's *Essays.*

Oliver Goldsmith (1728-1774) had a kindly heart and a lively sense of humour. The Common Soldier's sufferings remind us of the times when Goldsmith himself was in poverty and distress, and when he displayed the same optimistic spirit. His essays should be more widely read: some critics consider them to rank second only to those of Charles Lamb.

THE INN AT EVENING, from *The Path to Rome,* by Hilaire Belloc.

Joseph Hilaire Pierre Belloc was born in France in 1870 and was educated at the Oratory School, Birmingham, and Balliol College, Oxford. He has written essays, travel books, histories, poetry, and literary criticism.

The Path to Rome shows a wide range of interest and a genial humour.

A BULLY PUNISHED, from *The Romany Rye*, by George Borrow.

George Borrow (1803-1881) who travelled widely, knew many languages. His manner was open-hearted, so that he mixed freely with all kinds of folk; it is this which fills his books with interesting autobiographical detail. At times his style seems heavy, but this is forgotten in the variety of characters he depicts. Hugh Walker states: " It was Borrow who first gave gipsies a citizenship in literature."

IMPRESSIONS OF HOLLAND, from Lady Mary Wortley Montagu's *Letters*.

Lady Mary Wortley Montagu (1689-1762) was often celebrated by her famous contemporaries: Pope wrote verses about her; Kneller painted her portrait; the Kit-Kat Club drank toasts to her.

When her husband was appointed ambassador to Turkey she accompanied him. Noting the Turks' method of fighting small-pox by inoculation, she introduced this treatment into England.

Her letters are written in a sprightly style: often they rush on at a breathless pace, at once flippant and sincere, careless and sympathetic. Her wit has a pungency that gives rise to epigrams such as the famous, " General opinions are generally wrong," and " A face is too slight a foundation for happiness." Her love-letters are remarkably unsentimental.

GEYSERS, from *Letters from High Latitudes*, by Lord Dufferin.

Frederick Temple Hamilton Temple Blackwood, Marquis of Dufferin (1826-1902) was educated at Eton and Oxford. His book is written in a lively vein. It consists of letters to his mother telling of his adventures in the schooner *Foam* which visited Iceland, Spitzbergen, and the coast of Norway.

There are frequent passages of literary and historical interest. His descriptions of natural phenomena are both picturesque and colourful. He is fond of a jest: he tells his mother of a sea " as thickly crammed with ice as a lady's boudoir is with furniture." When a young Laplander falls in love he " goes off in search of a friend and a bottle of brandy."

PORTUGAL IN 1796, from Robert Southey's *Letters*.

Robert Southey (1774-1843) published his *Letters from Spain and Portugal* in 1797. It was the first of his many volumes of prose of which *The Life of Nelson* is the best known. His style is usually clear and easy-flowing. It is interesting to compare his descriptions of Portugal with those of Henry Fielding, the novelist, who wrote his *Journal of a Voyage to Lisbon* shortly before his death in 1754.

LAPLAND, from *The Story of San Michele*, by Alex Munthe.

Alex Munthe, a Swede, is a physician who took his doctor's degree in Paris. He now lives in retirement in a villa at San Michele in the Island of Capri.

It is impossible to say how far his book is autobiographical: he tells us that the best way to write one's autobiography is " to write a book . . . trying as hard as one can to think of somebody else."

His book will take you to many parts of Europe: often its exciting episodes will keep you in suspense.

A PARTY IN THE DESERT, from *Lawrence and the Arabs*, by Robert Graves.

Robert Ranke Graves (1895) was educated at Charterhouse and St. John's College, Oxford. He served in France with the Royal Welch Fusiliers. At one time he was Professor of English Literature at Cairo. He now lives in Spain.

In *Good-bye to All That* he tells of his experiences during and after the war. In Chapter XXVIII he describes his first meeting with T. E. Lawrence at a guest night at All Souls' College. Mr. George Bernard Shaw tried to dissuade Graves from writing a book on Lawrence, publication soon followed, and the book sold at the rate of ten thousand copies a week.

Mr. Graves has attained considerable distinction as a poet, but his most noteworthy work is the recently published *I Claudius*, which purports to be the autobiography of the Roman Emperor. Although its style is colloquial, the matter shows sound scholarship.

THE GREAT FIRE, from Evelyn's *Diary*.

John Evelyn (1620-1706) was a typical English country gentleman. At heart a Royalist, " his zeal was tempered with caution." Like King Charles II, he was an enthusiastic dabbler in science: he was one of the first Fellows of the Royal Society, founded in 1660. He was the lifelong friend of Pepys who, in 1664, also became a Fellow.

His diary is somewhat scrappy until 1641. From then it continues to be full of widely varied detail until three weeks before his death. As a document it is a valuable historical source for the period: to appreciate the spirit of those troublous times you should read his entries for the years 1666 and 1688.

A DAY IN THE COUNTRY, from Pepys's *Diary*.

Samuel Pepys (1632-1703) began his diary on 1st January, 1660, and made his last entry on 31st May, 1669, apparently in fear that his sight would fail. Though this calamity was averted, he made no further entries.

His diary, which was written in an old system of short-hand, was not deciphered until 1822. The MS. covered over 3,000 quarto pages. His is a more intimate diary than Evelyn's. Not only do we learn of the plays he saw, the music he loved, and his pride in his increasing prosperity, but we also find mention of his quarrels with his wife, and his practice of inflicting fines upon himself for falling into bad ways. He even records the number of lice found upon his head and body after his hair had been cut.

MY CORONATION, from *Queen Victoria's Journal*.

Queen Victoria (1819-1901) is here seen as a young woman setting down her naïve jottings. You should read Lytton Strachey's account of her long life and eventful reign.

THE DEATH OF CAPTAIN COOK, from *The Voyages of Captain Cook*.

James Cook (1728-1779) made three remarkable voyages of discovery. He was a singularly painstaking navigator, a great lover of mathematics and astronomy. He proved the existence of a huge Southern Continent and explored the full length of Eastern Australia. Not only did he make many discoveries among the islands in the southern Pacific, but he penetrated farther into the Antarctic than any previous navigator. His work created a new era in geographical science.

Almost of equal importance with these discoveries was his care for his men: it is said that scurvy became a thing of the past to those who sailed with him.

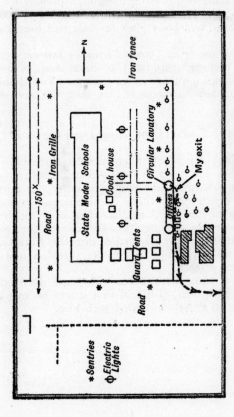

PLAN OF THE STATE MODEL SCHOOLS.

THE HERITAGE OF LITERATURE SERIES

TRAVEL AND ADVENTURE

Real Adventure.   SECTION A NO. 1
Captain Scott, Shackleton, Younghusband, Smythe, Mary Kingsley, Rex Clements, Fitzpatrick, Belloc, Tschiffely, Major Evans.

Creatures of the Wilds.   SECTION A NO. 2
Cherry Kearton, Eardley-Wilmot, Pienaar, Bullen, Haviland, Patterson, Millais, Munthe, Kingsley Fairbridge.

The Adventure of Travel.   SECTION A NO. 7
We invite you in this book to take a journey round the world in the company of modern travellers and explorers. There are a number of exciting as well as interesting incidents, such as: Peter Fleming's train crash in Siberia; a sham air raid over Mukden; Howard Carter's opening of Tut-ankh-Amen's tomb; Ponting's graphic description of the penguins; Shackleton's journey across South Georgia; F. S. Smythe's adventures with avalanches.

Eothen. By A. W. KINGLAKE.   SECTION B NO. 5
This classic of travel has been edited with notes and questions, an introduction and historical background to the book, and it includes a map and the author's original preface.

More Tales of Real Adventure.   SECTION A NO. 10
This volume brings the story of "Real Adventure" up to date. In it are described some of the most thrilling adventures of the present day, such as, the flight over the South Pole by Rear Admiral Byrd, the feat of the Citroen expedition in crossing the Himalayas in tractor cars, Nesbitt's arduous journey in the deserts of Abyssinian Danakil, and Bagnold's car ride in the Libyan Sands.

ESSAYS AND BELLES LETTRES

England Out of Doors.   SECTION A NO. 3
Galsworthy, Blunden, Lubbock, Viscount Grey, G. M. Trevelyan, Williamson, Sassoon, Cardus, de Selincourt and others.

Lighter Essays.   SECTION A NO. 5
Blunden, "Alpha of the Plough," Barbellion, R. L. Stevenson, Sir J. G. Frazer, W. H. Hudson, Robert Lynd, Goldsmith, Leigh Hunt and others.

Essays by Modern Writers.   SECTION B NO. 3
G. M. Trevelyan, Viscount Grey, Dr. Inge, Conrad, Blunden, Arthur Bryant, Rose Macaulay, Max Beerbohm, Robert Lynd, "Alpha of the Plough" and others.